D1638792

Series Editors: Andrew Arden QC and Caroline Hunter

Patrick Reddin FRICS, FBEng is the senior partner of Reddin & Nuttal, London. A Fellow of the Royal Institution of Chartered Surveyors, his experience extends over 30 years. A large part of his practice arises out of the diagnosis and rectification of building defects, including housing disrepair.

DEALING WITH DISREPAIR

A GUIDE TO INSPECTION AND DIAGNOSIS

Patrick Reddin

FRICS, FBEng

First published in Great Britain 1996 by

Lemos & Crane
20 Pond Square, Highgate
London N6 6BA

Telephone 0181 348 8263

ISBN 1-898001-06-5

A CIP catalogue record for this book is
available from the British Library.

Designed by Mick Keates.
Illustrations by Stephan Chabluk.
Typeset by Concise Artisans, London.
Printed by Redwood Books, Trowbridge.

ARDEN'S HOUSING LIBRARY

Series Editors: Andrew Arden QC and Caroline Hunter

"Ensuring the law is not just written but also
positively interpreted is important work.
I commend these titles."

Nick Raynsford MP, at the launch of Arden's Housing Library

"...an increasingly important series."
"The cumulative index is exceptionally good."

Housing (the journal of the Chartered Institute of Housing)

Volumes published in Arden's Housing Library

1 *Security of Tenure*
2 *Tenants' Rights*
3 *Nuisance and Harassment*
4 *Presenting Possession Proceedings*
5 *Repairs and Maintenance*
6 *Dealing with Disrepair*
7 *CCT of Housing Management (forthcoming)*

For more information about Arden's Housing Library,
please contact

Lemos & Crane
20 Pond Square
Highgate
London N6 6BA

Tel: 0181 348 8263
Fax: 0181 347 5740
Email: sales@lemos.demon.co.uk

Dedication

Claudio Sanjines Bastos 1978 to 1995

CONTENTS

FOREWORD by Andrew Arden QC   xii

INTRODUCTION   1

Part I. Understanding Buildings   5

1   HOUSING STOCK   7
Section A. Traditional   8
  External walls   10
    Solid brickwork   10
    Cavity brickwork   10
    Blockwork   11
  Internal walls   11
    Stud partitions   11
  Foundations   12
    Timber plates   12
    Brick footings   12
    Strip foundations   12
    Raft and other reinforced concrete foundations   13
    Piling   13
  Roofs   13
    Pitched roofs   13
      Valley roofs   13
      Front to rear pitched roofs   14
      Hips, valleys and gables   14
      Parapets, fire walls and chimneys   14
      Slates and tiles   15
    Flat roofs   16
  Floors   16
    Above ground level   16
    Timber ground floors   17
    Solid ground floors   17
    Boards and sheets   18
  Damp-proofing   18
    Walls   18
    Ground floors   19
    Basements   19
  Windows   19

Sliding sashes		19
Casements		19
Replacements		20
Section B. Non-Traditional		20
Steel and reinforced concrete framed		21
Large panel systems		21
No-fines		22
Modern timber-frame		22
2	MATERIALS OF CONSTRUCTION	23
	Timber	24
	Brick	26
	Mortar and pointing	28
	Render	28
	Insulation	29
	Rock	29
	Concrete	30
	Plaster	31
	Stone	31
	Slate	31
	Tiles	32
	Glass	32
	Metal	33
	Asphalt, felt and other bituminous materials	34
3	ENEMIES OF HEALTHY BUILDINGS	36
	Water	37
	Dampness from the ground	38
	Rising damp	38
	Lateral penetration	39
	Remedial damp-proofing	40
	Bridging	41
	Salts and residual dampness	42
	Above ground	43
	From above	44
	Cavity construction for walls	44
	From inside	45
	Condensation	45
	Interstitial condensation	46
	From construction	46
	Sulphates	46
	Fungi	47

Dry rot   47
Wet rot   48
Moulds   49
Insects   49
Wood-boring   49
Disease carrying   50
Just unpleasant   51
Metals   51
Hazardous materials   52
Asbestos   52
Removal contractors   52
Glass fibre   53
Urea-formaldehyde foam   53
Radon gas   53
Users   54
Moisture generation   54
Animals   55
Disease carrying   55
Refuse   55
Plants, trees and bushes   55
Temperature and climate   56
Drought   56
Frost   57
Snow   57
Sun   58
Underground threats   58
Non-traditional buildings   59
Prefabricated buildings   59
Large panel systems   59
High rise   60
Modern timber-framed buildings   61

Part II. Inspecting Disrepair   63

4   PREPARING FOR THE INSPECTION   65
Housing manager's role   65
Starting points   68
Occupied dwellings   68
Voids   68
Third parties   68
Is inspection necessary?   68

Recording information 69
    Recording the initial information 70
Background information 71
  Address and identification code 71
  Type of property 72
  Size and location 72
  Building type 72
  Occupants 72
  Tenancy agreement 73
  Common parts 73
Equipment 74
  Basics 74
  Moisture meter 75
    Camera 76

5 THE INSPECTION 77
Appointments and casual call systems 78
  Diary systems 79
Health and safety 80
Making appointments 81
Conducting the inspection 82
  Introductions 83
  Preliminaries 83
Methodical procedure 84
  Using the senses 86
  Identifying defects 86
Inspection notes 87
A practical illustration 94
Timescales 98
Do-It-Yourself 99

Part III. Post-Inspection Practice 101

6 REPORTING 103
Customers 104
The findings 104
Format 106
  Core section 106
  Supplementary sections 112
  Record note 112
  Landlord's liability 113

Tenant's liability 114
Reference to further action 114

7 PRIORITIES 115
External advice 116
Specification for repairs 116
Assessing priorities 117
General factors 117
Statutory obligations 119
Codes of practice 119
Tenants' Guarantee 120
Tenants' Right to Repair 120
Chartered Institute of Housing standards 122
Planned maintenance 122
Wholesale redevelopment or rehabilitation 123
Value for money 127

8 FOLLOW-UP ACTION 129
Monitoring performance 130
Management systems 131
Tenants' satisfaction surveys 131
Redecoration 132
Variations of the works 133
Longer-term action 135
Monitoring short-term repairs 136
Visits and revisits 136

9 COURT PROCEEDINGS 137
Instructing an expert 138
Expert evidence and advice 139
Choice of expert 141
Housing manager's evidence 142
Compliance with orders 142

10 CONCLUSION 144

APPENDIX I: Building diagrams 147

APPENDIX II: Diagnosing building defects 163

INDEX 169

xii

FOREWORD

by Andrew Arden QC

Patrick Reddin's *Dealing With Disrepair* is a somewhat different book from those which have hitherto appeared in the Housing Library.

Mr Reddin is a surveyor – there need be no secret of the matter, he is a very *good* surveyor, and he has for many years been my very good friend! For many years, he has also been the leading surveyor who has given expert evidence for tenants around the capital as to the repairs to which they are entitled. He has enjoyed a remarkable, perhaps unparalleled, court-room success. And he has been highly active in the repair and improvement (and construction) of social housing. In this book, he has sought to bring together his twin areas of long experience, so as to enable housing managers to do their jobs in a way that accords with their tenants' legal rights, and ensure that those rights do not cut across the way that they wish to do their jobs.

The genesis of the book, and its purpose, does not, however, exist in isolation. Disrepair is not merely about decay and works that are desirable in the owner's eyes – in this case, social landlords. It is also about the legal rights of occupiers: landlords' freedom to choose what works they do to their properties is limited; the first call on their resources is that which is dictated by the law, primarily in support of the rights of occupiers to a physically sound home. This book, therefore, is but one half of the equation: the other is represented by *Repairs and Maintenance*, by Alyson Kilpatrick. The purpose of this Foreword is to explain their connection.

Alyson Kilpatrick's book, in one sense, is but one more in the Housing Library through which we have sought to evolve the notion that – in a climate of reduced public expenditure available *both* for housing itself *and* for tenants or other occupiers to enjoy access to qualified advice and assistance to enforce their rights – it is important for housing managers to ensure that their actions are legally correct from the outset, instead of relying on a corrective response from occupiers: see "Social Housing: Moving from Litigation to Managerial Prevention of Errors," *Leading Edge* (Lemos & Crane Occasional Briefing, No. 1; also reproduced as the Series Foreword in S. Belgrave *Nuisance and Harassment*, Vol. 3 in the Library).

In the case of disrepair, this message is, perhaps, more important than in any other. If the property of social landlords falls into disrepair, then a court will order works on an individual unit basis, and may well award substantial sums of damages to the individual tenant (and costs of legal representation which may likewise prove substantial). There has, indeed, been some media attention paid to the phenomenon, in consequence of which some local authorities have found that significant proportions of their maintenance budgets have gone, not – as intended – to planned or preventative maintenance, but to reactive repairs, compensation and costs, with the consequence that large-scale, estate-wide programmes have not been able to proceed. For cyclical repairs, read cycle of frustration and decay.

In times of severly constrained expenditure, one is bound to feel considerable sympathy for social landlords who bemoan this Catch-22: if they await the programme, the individual complainant can use the law to achieve a priority that in turn delays improved conditions for others; yet, there is not the money to bring forward the programme. There is, of course, no grand solution – other than for the government to provide more money or else to lower legal standards (as, e.g., most mandatory grants in respect of unfit property are due to be repealed when the Housing Grants, etc., Bill becomes law). The first appears to be out of the question; to resort to the second would be some kind of ultimate defeat for those who have committed themselves to the provision of decent, social housing; to allow our difficulties to persuade us to support any such regression would be to turn upon our own.

Yet just because there is no grand solution does not mean that there is nothing that can be done to mitigate a difficult problem. There is. If housing managers are actively aware of what legal *rights* tenants and other occupiers enjoy, below which their standards cannot fall without the risk of costly litigation and even costlier reactive repairs, they can better allocate their resources – financial and human – to ensure that there is a sustainable balance between those rights and the needs of the programme. At one extreme, throwing all

one's resources into the programme could render it
vulnerable to upset as a result of a single substantial
claim (of which legal costs alone may be a significant
proportion); at the other, throwing all one's resources
into individual claims is a form of crisis management
that can only, in the longer term, postpone and exacer-
bate the problem.

To illustrate: one (large) social landlord established a
Task Force, to ring-fence and react *immediately* to complaints of disrepair which appeared to be capable of
pursuit to law (whether by way of civil action in the
county court, or criminal action for statutory nuisance
in the magistrates' court): within days, property would
be visited, those works to which it was considered
there was a legal entitlement to an immediate order
were commissioned, and within – at the outside –
weeks, they were executed. Contemporaneously, an
offer of compensation was made, representing a fair –
but not excessive – sum for the period in question.
Likewise, legal costs (if any) *to date* were offered.
Actions that traditionally had led to consequences –
globally – in the five figures could be contained in the
low fours. Meanwhile, the longer-term works could be
absorbed in the next appropriate programme.

What was imaginative about this solution was the
admixture of legal and building professional skills. A
lawyer worked in the Task Force, to advise on what
works would be the subject of an immediate order, and
what would represent fair compensation and an appropriate payment for costs; surveyors advised the lawyer
on the condition of the property, the consequences and
implications, and organised the maintenance crews; it
was a team response to a multi-disciplinary activity

that *could* not await the normal "channels of communication and co-operation" without generating a financial consequence that took the landlord straight (back) into that cycle of frustration and decay to which I referred above.

This book and Ms Kilpatrick's accordingly mirror the theme of this series (and this Foreword) by explaining to housing managers how to identify disrepair, and to commission its remedy, in the context of the legal framework by which the subject is governed. Between them, these books and their authors have taken forward the notion that "prevention is better than cure," in two disciplines, entirely different conceptually, but entirely dependent on each other for their daily application. This one is the practice; Ms Kilpatrick's book, the theory.

Andrew Arden QC
Arden Chambers
59 Fleet Street
London EC4Y 1JU

ARDEN

A

CHAMBERS

INTRODUCTION

This book is for managers of rented housing. It helps them to identify and diagnose disrepair and to find remedies to deal with it. For tenants, the landlord's housing managers are the first point of contact. Increasingly, managers have to face complaints of disrepair; and this book equips them fully to assess and deal with such problems.

The first three chapters describe the various ways in which houses have been constructed: the qualities of materials used in buildings and the common causes of disrepair. Chapters 4 and 5 give the reader the tools and techniques for inspecting and diagnosing disrepair. The next three chapters explain how to report back on what has been diagnosed; where more professional help may be needed; and the legal obligations and financial constraints that often conflict with carrying out repairs work. Chapter 8 shows how to follow through and ensure that appropriate repairs have actually been done. Chapter 9 comes in where all else fails – covering the process of litigation in the courts.

There are increasing pressures on social landlords who are trying to sustain a well-maintained housing stock. Tenants' aspirations are rising. Government funding is falling. Much of the stock was badly designed to begin with, and has already passed its planned lifespan. The demands are overwhelming. But failure to carry out repairs is even more costly – eating away at the capital value of the stock, while generating expensive and time-consuming litigation on the way.

In response to these enormous pressures, the social landlord can at least ensure that disrepair is dealt with through top quality management procedures. The modern business concept of quality has refocused relationships with external customers such as tenants. But it has also created new demands for professionals from different disciplines to work together effectively as a team within established written procedures which are monitored in practice. All this is a prerequisite for those who strive for the European Standard of Quality Assurance (ISO 9001), conceived as a means of helping to build the effective systems which this new outlook demands.

Dealing with Disrepair is a book essentially about structural disrepair. It is not concerned with defects to services such as heating systems, gas supply and electricity, except insofar as they have implications for the fitness and structural soundness of the dwelling. The book is intended not just as an initial source of information, but as a point of continuing reference. The appendices include illustrations of the different parts of buildings (Appendix I, pp. 147-162). The book has been written in parallel with A. Kilpatrick's *Repairs and Maintenance: law and practice in the management of social housing* (Ardens' Housing Library vol. 5, 1996) which covers the legislative framework in detail.

Structural disrepair, however, has more than one meaning because the word "structure" is open to different interpretations. For architects and surveyors something is "structural" if it supports, strengthens or restrains the basic frame of the building – like load-bearing walls, floor joists and roof timbers.

In relation to disrepair, there is another way of looking at the meaning of "structure". In this view, every part of the structure – wall, roof, floor, and so on – is made up of elements which only together make up a whole. Many walls have brick as their core, and this may be covered by a vapour barrier or insulation, which in turn is covered by plaster, lining-paper and paint. At some point, moving out from the basic structural brickwork, components are no longer structural but are simply part of the interior or decoration. This borderline is the most common demarcation between the respective repairing liabilities of landlord and tenant. This book explains how these elements fit together to form the whole of the structure.

PART I

UNDERSTANDING BUILDINGS

CHAPTER 1

HOUSING STOCK

SECTION A. TRADITIONAL

External walls /*Solid brickwork* / *Cavity brickwork* / **Blockwork** / **Internal walls** / *Stud partitions* / **Foundations** / *Timber plates* / *Brick footings* / *Strip foundations* / *Raft and other reinforced concrete foundations* / *Piling* / **Roofs** / *Pitched roofs* / *Flat roofs* / **Floors** / *Above ground level* / *Timber ground floors* / *Solid ground floors* / *Boards and sheets* / **Damp-proofing** / *Walls* / *Ground floors* / *Basements* / **Windows** / *Sliding sashes* / *Casements* / *Replacements*

SECTION B. NON-TRADITIONAL

Steel and reinforced concrete framed / **Large panel systems** / *No-fines* / **Modern timber-frame** / **Special buildings** / *Prefabricated buildings* / *Large panel systems* / *High rise* / *Modern timber-framed buildings*

Buildings are an integral part of the housing manager's work. They are the main piece of equipment used by the manager to house the tenants. In order to appreciate, work with and even enjoy the study of and use of buildings, the housing manager needs to have an understanding of the various types of housing in the

UK and the methods and components of construction.

The UK housing stock is commonly divided into two categories, traditional and non-traditional. Until the late 1960s this was an easy distinction to draw. The two categories were largely identifiable by their appearance with no need for analysis of background information. Repairs problems and solutions were generally considered to be common to all types of buildings within each of these categories. This was, regrettably, an over-simplification. Housing managers must go into the subject in more depth if they are to identify areas of risk for disrepair and come up with repair solutions.

This chapter describes the characteristics of both types and the signs to look for to enable further identification within each group. The defects inherent or likely to occur with each type are discussed in chapter 2.

SECTION A. TRADITIONAL

We describe a building which is over 250 years old not as "traditional", but as "historic" or merely "old". What then do we mean by the term "traditional"? The great urban building boom came in the early and mid-Victorian era in the wake of the industrial revolution, when the once rural population came flooding into the towns. The first urban response to this demand from city dwellers was from the speculative private sector.

Multi-occupied tenement blocks and rows of back-to-back terraced units were constructed in the very heart of our major conurbations.

The poor living conditions within these dwellings, with shared sanitary facilities and inadequate supplies of drinking water, soon gave rise to severe health problems and fears of a new plague.

Pressure from churches, charities and benevolent industrial owners resulted in the introduction of public health laws and the establishment of the social housing movement. This led to the construction of a vast number of dwellings in the latter part of the 19th century and the first 40 years of this century. This style, now referred to as traditional, has continued to be built, although in declining numbers, to the present day.

The pressure to deliver dwellings fast after the Armistice in 1918 fell to the public sector. A target of 500,000 dwellings in three years was set in the Housing and Town Planning Act 1919. Subsequent legislation in 1923 and 1924 produced another 503,000 units. The emphasis in the 1930s shifted to slum clearance and between 1935 and 1938, for example, 400,000 dwellings were produced.

However, if we examine the styles and methods of construction used over this period of perhaps 70 years, we find varied and significantly different qualities. These can be compared by looking at each element in turn and assessing the differences which have significance in terms of current maintenance and repair. Dates and periods given can only be rough guides. Innovation and varying styles throughout the UK resulted in widespread divergence of house styles and types and methods of construction.

External walls

Solid brickwork (Appendix I – fig. 1.1 – p. 148)
Prior to 1900, walls were almost exclusively of solid brickwork. They were constructed of bricks laid one on top of another in a regular pattern to ensure that no joints ran vertically through more than one layer (course). The bricks were bedded in mortar, incorporating lime which allowed some flexibility for structural movement. With the mortar joint, the brick dimensions were 112 (4½˝) thick x 75mm (3˝) high x 225mm (9˝) wide. This solid brickwork was commonly 225mm (9˝) thick for buildings of two storeys increasing to 337 (13½˝) thick to the lower floors where three or four storeys were constructed. Higher quality construction, for the merchant classes, commonly had a basement with 450mm (18˝) thick walls.

Cavity brickwork (Appendix I – fig. 1.2 – p. 148)
From about 1900, there was an increasing use of cavity wall construction and of masonry other than bricks. The use of cavity construction in the early part of this century is commonly found in Hampshire whereas elsewhere, for example in London, it is rare to find it in dwellings built before 1925.

Cavity walls comprise of two skins of masonry, tied together with metal at regular intervals. The cavity was open at top and bottom to allow air to circulate. It assumed that rainwater could in exposed areas breach the outer skin of brickwork. The ventilation of the cavity and the formation of twists and drips on the metal ties prevented transmission to the interior skin to keep the dwelling dry.

Blockwork (Appendix I – fig. 1.3 – p. 148)

The pressure to deliver large quantities of dwellings in the period from 1919 to 1938, together with a reduced and ill-prepared construction materials industry, triggered the more innovative manufacturers of materials and house designers to look at new alternatives to brick. The main innovation was the block. This was usually of the same thickness as the brick but 450mm (18″) x 225mm (9″). Its larger size allowed speedier construction, thus reducing labour costs and time.

Blocks became increasingly used for the inner skin of cavity walls. They were also used for exteriors where these were to be rendered.

Internal walls

Stud partitions (Appendix I – fig. 2.1 – p. 149)

Prior to 1925, the most common form of construction for internal walls was a timber stud partition. The timbers (studs) are arranged vertically at approximately 400 to 500mm (16″ to 18″) with horizontal timbers (plates) at the top and bottom. Between the studs, timber noggins are installed to prevent lateral movement, and in more substantial construction diagonal bracing is also included.

It is a common fallacy that these timber walls do not carry any loads. Invariably they are load-bearing and the only safe assumption is that they are an essential part of the structure of the building until they can be shown to have no structural significance. From about 1925, internal walls, particularly load-bearing walls, were constructed of brick or block (Appendix I – figs. 2.2 & 1.3).

Foundations

Timber plates (Appendix I – fig. 3.1 – p. 151)

Early dwellings, i.e. pre-1800, were often built directly off the ground with a base layer of stones on which was laid a timber plate. Secondhand ships' timbers were commonly used, the pitch applied for sea use giving good resistance to dampness, and fungal or insect attack.

Brick footings (Appendix I – fig. 3.2 – p. 151)

Most of today's rented housing stock will have, as a minimum, brick footings. They comprise of two or more courses of bricks laid wider than the width of the wall onto broken stone or compressed ground to spread the load of the wall. The more courses and the greater the spread, the lower the pressure on the ground and therefore less likelihood of failure.

Unfortunately these footings tend to be shallow and, although adequate to distribute the load from the wall to the soil, are incapable of resisting the pressures exerted by tree roots, sub-soil movement and changing water content.

Strip foundations (Appendix I – figs. 3.3a & 3.3b – p. 152)

To overcome the problems of ground movement, concrete strip foundations came into common use by about 1930. The concrete, usually about 300mm thick, is laid at a depth of about 1m and will be three times the width of the wall. The depth is to overcome the effects of frost on the ground. In many cases these foundations are adequate, but as with brick footings, sub-soil movement, such as settlement or subsidence and tree roots can undermine and destabilise them.

Raft and other reinforced concrete foundations (Appendix I – figs. 3.4a & 3.4b – p. 153)

Where ground stability is known to be a problem, steel is introduced into the foundations to increase strength and elasticity. In some cases, rather than excavate to a great depth to find good ground from which to build, reinforced concrete slabs are laid from which the super-structure can be erected. In effect, these rafts are deep, reinforced concrete floor slabs, spreading the load of the superstructure over the site.

Piling (Appendix I – fig. 3.5 – p. 154)

Where ground conditions are unstable, piled foundations are used. These foundations transfer the loads of the building deep into the ground onto sound bearings. The caps to the piled foundations which are reinforced with steel are linked together either in a series of beams or as a slab (rather like a raft).

Roofs

Pitched roofs (Appendix I – fig. 4.1 – p. 155)

Pitched roofs are all those with sloping faces, draining down to a gutter. Almost without exception, the structures of these roofs have been constructed of timber.

Valley roofs (Appendix I – fig. 4.2 – p. 156)

In central urban areas, particularly in London, there was an architectural demand to form a level and decorated parapet to the front elevation. To employ a roof sloping down to the front with an external gutter would have made this stylistic demand unattainable.

The solution was the centre valley, or butterfly roof. This comprised a central timber beam, often made up of two parallel timbers, supported on the front and rear external walls with part of the load transmitted down onto the central stud partition.

Front to rear pitched roofs (Appendix I – fig. 4.2 – p. 156)

These are the most common type of roof found on UK housing prior to 1945. The roof structure comprises of rafters much like floor joists but laid to a slope. These are often supported by purlins, larger timbers running across the slope, in turn supported on struts down to the internal walls.

Hips, valleys and gables (Appendix I – fig. 4.1 – p. 155)

Where parts of the building are constructed on differing planes, the roof junctions are formed with hips (outer angles) and valleys (inner angles). Where roofs come to vertical face, the triangular vertical panel is called a gable, regardless of its material.

All changes in direction and junctions are areas of increased vulnerability.

Parapets, fire walls and chimneys (Appendix I – fig. 4.1 – p. 155)

In modern construction, the front to rear roof on a terrace of houses is constructed separately for each house. Between the houses the separating wall, usually of brick, rises to above roof level as a parapet. In Inner London, building by-laws have required this parapet for almost 100 years, but outside this area, the wall commonly stops at the underside of the roof.

In terraced housing before 1925, it was also common

to leave out bricks in the separating wall within the loft. This permitted cross-ventilation throughout the whole terrace and was intended to minimise condensation and to remove minor dampness resulting from intermittent water penetration.

Slates and tiles (Appendix I – fig. 4.1 – p. 155)

In urban areas, roofs were covered with slate. Slate quarries in Wales and other parts of the UK were at their zenith in the mid-19th century, with demand exceeding supply year on year. The inability of the slate quarries to satisfy demand led to the more widespread use of clay tiles, hitherto confined to localised manufacture. Large-scale tile production alongside bricks and blocks ensured a constant and adequate supply of material for the inter-war building boom.

Tiles are not as durable as good quality slate, but are not dissimilar to the poorer slates produced to satisfy the periods of heavy demand at low price. Tiles were, and still are, cheaper than slate, and the supply seems inexhaustible, being independent of the natural occurrence of suitable rock.

In the context of building defects, the primary distinction to be noted is the weight of the material and the consequent additional strength of the structure required to support it.

In the early 1970s it was a common practice to renew slate roof coverings with concrete tiles. The increased weight called for additional support to the roof structure but this was not always provided. After a series of roof collapses, regulations were clarified, making the change in material a notifiable operation under the building regulations.

With the development of bituminous felts and plastic materials, particularly after 1945, under-slate/tile coverings were installed. These provide a secondary barrier to wind-blown rain and snow.

Flat roofs (Appendix I – fig. 5.1 – p. 157)

Flat roofs were rare before 1930 and not in common use until after the Second World War. More recent additions to existing buildings may have flat roofs.

Flat roofs are less capable of shedding water than sloping roofs and are more susceptible to thermal movements. The coverings are therefore put under greater stress, causing earlier failure and reducing the life of the roof.

The coverings are of metal (usually zinc or lead) (Appendix I – fig. 5.1) or of asphalt or bituminous felt (Appendix I – fig. 5.2a). These coverings are applied over a structure which can be of timber, reinforced concrete or steel. In housing, steel is rare and in the main concrete roofs are limited to non-traditional construction or to blocks of flats rather than houses.

Today, flat roofs are required to have properly designed and constructed insulation to minimise heat loss, vapour barriers to minimise the risk of moisture condensing within the structure, and ventilation to release any entrapped water vapour.

Floors

Above ground level (Appendix I – fig. 6.1 – p. 159)

These have consistently been of timber, except in larger buildings and more recent domestic construction where sound reduction and fire separation have made other materials more viable.

The floor structure consists of joists spanning between load-bearing walls. The direction of span will usually be the shortest distance. Where boards are visible, the joists run at 90° to the boards. As with the roof, loads are carried not just by masonry walls but also by internal partitions. In some construction, especially in 1930s semi-detached two-storey suburban housing, floors span the shortest distance in each room, thus requiring all walls to be load-bearing.

Timber ground floors (Appendix I – fig. 6.2 – p. 159)

These are of similar design to the upper floors. Instead of being supported on the external and other load-bearing walls, they are supported on small walls in the space below the floor. These walls, known as sleeper walls, are built off the ground or off a "blinding" a thin covering of concrete, and are surmounted by timber plates onto which the joists sit.

Solid ground floors (Appendix I – fig. 6.3 – p. 160)

Where excavation below the lowest floor was not feasible, or too expensive, solid floors were used. These were commonly of stone slabs with joints filled with mortar until 1874 (see Damp-proofing below). Poured concrete became the common material, laid on a bed of hardcore and finished with quarry tiles or a cement screed laid onto a damp-proof membrane.

Replacement floors, when original timber floors have failed, are commonly constructed of concrete where the depth for ventilation below the floor is inadequate.

Boards and sheets (Appendix I – fig. 6.2 – p. 159)
Until about 1960, flooring was usually of boards laid across and nailed down to the joists. Thicknesses varied and in the late inter-war period and early 1950s, tongued and grooved boarding was common, intended to minimise warping and draughts. In the last 30 to 35 years, sheet materials, particularly chipboard, have become commonplace.

Damp-proofing (Appendix I – figs. 6.2 & 6.3 – pp. 159-160)

Damp-proofing has been a requirement for parts of houses since 1875. (See Public Health Act 1875 section 157.) Dampness in this context is restricted to moisture entering the building from the enclosing or supporting ground. It does not include other penetrating or condensation-caused dampness which are discussed in chapter 3.

Walls (Appendix I – figs. 1.1-1.3 – p. 148)
Physical barriers in walls are installed to prevent ground moisture rising up to the level of occupation, usually the ground floor. The earliest materials were over-burned bricks, and later superseded by slate, tiles, water-resistant engineering bricks, bituminous compounds, asphalt, metals and plastics. From 1874, any residential building was constructed with the intention that it should provide a barrier to ground moisture. Whether it was built with one or not is a matter of fact but it should be presumed that it was unless shown otherwise.

Ground floors (Appendix I – fig. 6.2 – p. 159)
The lowest floor also required a barrier against ground moisture. In timber floors this was by means of a damp-proof course below the timber plates or within the sleeper walls.

In solid floors (Appendix I – fig. 6.3) it could be the stone slabs themselves or a quarry tile finish. In concrete floors a membrane of bitumen, asphalt or, latterly, plastic was laid below a screed or floor finish.

Basements

Where the floor level is below external ground level, damp-proofing must include a form of tanking to be effective. Tanking is a vertical barrier against penetration of dampness, linked to the horizontal barriers in the floor and walls to form a watertight envelope.

Windows

Sliding sashes (Appendix I – fig. 7.1 – p. 160)
Until the 1920s, vertical sliding sashes were the most common type of window for dwellings. They comprise a timber frame with cavities in which weights are suspended on cords to counter-balance the weight of the glazed timber sash, which moves up and down. The vertical axis is longer than the horizontal.

On more modern sliding sash windows, spring balances are used to replace cords. Although cheaper, they fail more frequently and require adjustment.

Casements (Appendix I – fig. 7.2 – p. 161)
These are of either timber or steel (a common trade

name being Crittall). They are usually rectangular in overall shape with a longer horizontal axis. Opening sections are hinged and have catches and stays to lock them in position.

Replacements

With an ageing housing stock, replacement windows must be expected. These may be of the same pattern as the original but are more commonly of a cheaper and more readily available type. For example, sliding sash windows are replaced with top-hung casements (Appendix I – fig. 7.2) or louvres (Appendix I – fig. 7.5). In the last 20 years plastic windows have become more widespread offering cheapness combined with durability and a promise of low-maintenance costs.

SECTION B. NON-TRADITIONAL

Although not exclusively so, the majority of these dwellings are in the social housing sector, primarily in local authority developments. This was the sector which bore the pressure for production of high quantities of housing both between the wars and after the Second World War. It was the sector with money available in return for quantity and short-term solutions. Housing was never given a life-span beyond 60 years and commonly 30 years has been translated unofficially as in perpetuity. Except in rare instances, social housing blocks of flats were of traditional construction until after 1945.

The theories of 1930s architects and social engineers throughout Europe had seen high-rise structures used for commercial buildings. The structural qualities of steel and concrete enabled the engineers to design and build these multi-storey buildings. It only required the architect to design an aesthetically acceptable facade and a single standard floor layout to produce a product offering simplicity, predictability and ease of repetition.

Steel and reinforced concrete frame

These were developed mainly in the inter-war and immediate post-war years. The characteristics are a factory-made appearance without the dimensions or proportions of brick buildings. Large panels were often used to clad the exterior and lightweight roof coverings are fitted on minimal load-bearing structural components.

Large panel systems

The 1950s urge to build coupled with the shortage of skilled labour fulfilled the long-held dream of builders to apply mass-production factory techniques to the construction industry. This could be best achieved by prefabrication and limiting site work to assembly. The large panel systems, marketed by various contractors under patent names, were the epitome of factory production in this period.

These systems were used for both low-rise and high-rise blocks and, although considerably out of favour, are still within the nation's housing stock.

No-fines

No-fines concrete was used in the 1950s and 1960s for housing. The concrete is, as its title implies, without fines, i.e. sand and fine aggregate. The benefits of this are greater thermal insulation and speed of construction.

The outer face of the walls is rendered and it is only the subtle regularity and absence of any sign of brick or block beneath the render that gives the visual clue to its construction.

Modern timber-frame

The development of modern timber-framed construction began in the 1960s and the construction of significant numbers of dwellings commenced in the mid-1970s. The structural part of the walls is a timber frame, treated against fungal and insect attack and protected by a water-proofing membrane. The exterior is clad with a brick skin, in much the same way as the traditional cavity wall, with steel ties anchored into the timber structure. The external appearance is therefore of traditional construction but, as will be seen in chapter 3, very different defects can arise.

The tell-tale signs of timber-framed construction are the overall thickness of the walls, usually no more than a traditional cavity wall, 275mm (11´´), but with hollow plasterboard linings to the inside face.

CHAPTER 2

MATERIALS OF CONSTRUCTION

Timber / Brick / Mortar and pointing / Render / Insulation / Rock / Concrete / Plaster / Stone / Slate / Tiles / Glass / Metal / Asphalt, felt and other bituminous materials

Materials used for buildings may often appear to be inert. However, we have yet to develop materials for common use which are not adversely affected by the earth's natural environment. This chapter examines the nature of the primary materials from which we continue to build houses.

If you do not know about the materials of construction, you will not understand either the nature or significance of a defect, or how a particular part of the building contributes to the overall performance of the dwelling as a shelter.

It is suggested that one of the marks of modern society and perhaps of civilisation is that we have sophisticated organisations and solutions to common human problems. We have evolved a system of construction intended to provide healthy buildings within which we work and live, shielded from the elements. This basic need to be protected from natural risks and phenomena has been recognised as a primary demand with the provision of a home being elevated almost to a basic human right, alongside liberty and freedom of expression. The question of whether a building can perform the function for which it was intended is always a relevant consideration.

A building is like an onion, with one layer covering another. This chapter examines what materials are used, how things are put together and what the enemies of those materials and elements can do.

Appendix II sets out in more detail the analysis of defects from the initial appearance through to the identification of the primary cause (see pp. 163-167).

Timber

Probably the most commonly found material in residential buildings, timber has been the basic material for construction since humans relinquished the natural shelter of caves.

Timber comes from trees and is classified under two headings: hardwood and softwood. These groups are named not for the inherent feel of the timber, although in some cases that follows the name, but because of the structure of the wood. For example, pine is a softwood, quite hard and durable, but Balsa, malleable, soft and compressible, is a hardwood.

Hardwoods take longer to grow and generally are not capable of replacement at anything like the rate they are used. Softwoods tend to be fast-growing and renewable. With the realisation that the earth's resources are running out, builders have steered away from hardwoods except for particular uses where no alternative is suitable.

Timber is seasoned, i.e. dried, to a low moisture content prior to use. The lowering of the moisture content reduces the risk of warping and shrinkage once it is installed in a dwelling and the heating is turned on. It also reduces the moisture content to a level at which it is insufficient to promote or sustain fungal growth.

In domestic buildings, softwoods predominate. The nature and quality of the timber will vary. Older buildings, particularly in the mid-Victorian period, used well-seasoned softwoods, durable and resistant to fungal and insect attack (see below). As building production increased in the late Victorian era and at various times this century, the demand for good, well-seasoned timber has out-stripped supply. To satisfy demand, younger or less durable softwoods have been used.

After years of problems with fungus and insects, the building industry accepted that poorer quality timber could be used only if it were treated with chemicals. Today, almost all softwoods used in buildings are pre-treated with chemicals to hinder the ravages of fungus and insects.

Timber is used in two qualities in construction. The cruder and un-planed timber is used for the structure, the floors, the roofs and the parts which will not be seen when completed. This does not permit the builder to use lower grade or strength of timber, merely that which is not smoothed to an aesthetically acceptable finish.

The planed timber, shaved to a smooth surface ready

for staining or painting, is used for the visible joinery in the building, ranging from floorboards to furniture.

The excess of demand over supply with consequent increases in timber prices has also led to the search for new materials using otherwise rejected chippings, off-cuts, etc. Composite, factory-made timber materials are now commonly found in buildings.

The most common is probably particle board (the generic term for chip-board, laminboard and a myriad of others). These boards are manufactured with off-cuts, shavings and otherwise rejected pieces of sound timber, mixed and bonded together with resin to form a dense and solid mass. The density of the boards varies from highly compressed hardboard to soft insulation board.

These boards are used for flooring, kitchen units, shelving, doors and mouldings. Although different to natural timber, they have the same properties and vulnerabilities to fungus and insects.

Brick

In the UK we have large deposits of clay. Clay when baked forms a hard, dense and stable material which can resist the effects of rain, temperature and humidity changes. Since Roman times bricks have been used for better quality housing. Modern bricks are manufactured to regular sizes and achieve a remarkable degree of standardisation of quality, thanks primarily to the improvement in oven-baking techniques.

Clay bricks are at their driest when they leave the kiln. From that point they will absorb moisture, although the extent of absorption will diminish with time. As the moisture content varies so will their size, causing movement within the structure.

In more recent years, other materials such as calcium silicate have been used for bricks. Unlike clay bricks, the movement of these is primarily generated by drying rather than wetting. Their use in the ground therefore presents no problems, but above ground severe movement can occur.

In the 19th century it was still necessary to have a skilled assessor of bricks to select those which were of better quality and to allocate those inferior bricks to a suitable task. Today, this selection is made not from each batch but from the catalogue.

Because of the regularity of size and shape, bricklaying has become cheaper and faster. Today, notwithstanding the increasing use of other structural materials, brick is still holding its own as a major constituent of domestic buildings.

Bricks vary in density and strength. Some are extremely dense and almost impervious. These can be used as a damp-proof course or for below-ground work where dampness cannot be avoided. Above ground, less dense bricks are used which have varying degrees of porosity.

High density impervious bricks are expensive to produce, so lower density bricks are far more common. Buildings are designed to accommodate this, just as cavity walls assume the possibility of water penetrating the outer skin of brickwork.

In most cities, older buildings are built of 225mm (9″) brickwork (i.e. one brick thick). If these walls were in an exposed position, or where there is a defect such as a leaking rainwater pipe allowing water to saturate the exterior, then water penetration to the interior is likely. Thicker solid walls, denser bricks and cavity construction are all factors which will improve the walls' resistance to such water penetration.

Mortar and pointing

When built as a wall, bricks are bedded in mortar. This is a composition of cement, lime and sand in varying proportions. The mix, with water, is designed to hold the bricks together yet to allow some flexibility. However, more modern mortar mixes are often hard. Whereas with older buildings some structural movement can be accommodated, in modern structures every slight distortion can be marked by a crack.

When pointing is missing, soft or perished, water can enter the top surface of the brick. Combined with frost action, this will lead to breakage of the brick and increase the possibility of water penetrating to the interior.

Render

Cement mixes are often applied to the outside of buildings. In some cases this is for aesthetic reasons only, but more usually it is to provide a weather-proofing function. The mix will, like mortar, be of cement, lime and sand and should provide a flexible surface. Again in modern times, hard, inflexible render mixes have been used. Crazing of render with minor, non-structural cracks will occur with less flexible mixes or where the render is stronger than the brickwork on which it is applied. This crazing will allow water to penetrate and, coupled with frost action, will cause deterioration of the brickwork often before the render itself shows signs of any serious failure.

Insulation

Modern buildings are required by the Building Regulations to achieve a minimum insulation value. For cavity walls, this is usually achieved by the insertion of insulation in the cavity. The materials commonly used are rock fibre (fibre glass), polyurethane foam and urea-formaldehyde foam.

Urea-formaldehyde foam has achieved some notoriety for discharging gases into the dwellings. The chemical reaction of the two agents which make up the foam releases formaldehyde gas. The cavity must be well ventilated at its head so that this gas escapes.

Other risks with insulation in cavity walls arise from bridging of the cavity allowing rainwater to pass from the exterior to the interior (see chapter 3).

With solid walls, internal or external insulation is applied over the brick. The increased thermal efficiency will be risk free only if any such insulation takes full account of moisture passing through the wall.

Rock

Rocks, either cut or crushed, supply a main source of building material. When used as a prime material without chemical conversion, rocks are commonly termed stone (see below).

Concrete

The chemical conversion of crushed stone into cement was perfected in the last century. Today, there is a multitude of different cements which are used to make concrete. In all cases the cement is mixed with sand and stones (together called aggregate) and water. The mixing produces both a physical blend and a chemical change which causes the cement to heat and cure into a hard and durable material.

In most domestic buildings Ordinary Portland Cement is the main constituent of concrete. It develops its strength over a week or two. It has little resistance to acids or sulphates and may not always be used below ground where sulphate-resistant concrete is required.

Other cement mixes achieve more rapid hardening or are especially resistant to acid or sulphate attack.

High Alumina Cement was rarely used prior to the 1950s. Its attraction was that it developed very high strength within 24 hours, thus speeding up the building process. It was particularly used in factory manufacture of pre-fabricated beams. After placing, High Alumina Cement concrete undergoes a chemical change known as conversion. This will result in a reduction in strength over five or 10 years. When converted the concrete is vulnerable to acid, sulphate and alkali attack. After 10 years, some slight increase in strength occurs, but in warm, moist situations, further chemical action is possible depending on the aggregates used.

Plaster

The principal reason for applying plaster to wall surfaces is to conceal the unavoidable irregular surfaces of the structure itself. Plastering achieves this by filling the gaps and levelling out the surface. It also adds to the thermal efficiency of the wall or ceiling and to the sound reduction.

Where a wall has been damp, for example where affected by rising damp, specialist plasters are applied to resist the passage of residual salts to the interior, which will damage the decorations.

Stone

Stone is the term commonly applied to rock which is not chemically converted or otherwise restructured. It is rock which is cut from the natural source and split and shaped (dressed) and then used in its natural state as a building material.

Stone has been used for thousands of years as a building material. Although thought of as inert, stone may contain organic material and varies from very dense and strong (e.g. granite) to soft and porous (e.g. sandstone). The durability will vary significantly from one quarry site to another.

Slate

Slate is also a stone and has been used for many years as a roofing material and as a damp-proofing medium.

Due to its high cost and finite resources, imitation slates have been manufactured. Until the mid-1970s these were primarily of asbestos-cement but today are of cement and mineral fibres.

Deterioration is generally slow and is aggravated by air pollution. Natural slate should have a life expectancy of between 50 and 80 years and imitation slate perhaps 40 to 70 years. More likely than slow deterioration due to age is breakage of the slates by impact or corrosion of the metal fixings. With old slate roofs, iron nails fixed through the slates will have corroded well within the lifespan of the slate causing the slates to slip. This is sometimes known as nail sickness. More modern roofs should have fixings of non-ferrous metals which will be less affected by corrosion.

Tiles

Tiles for roof covering are made from clay and from concrete. The latter is cheaper and nowadays is the primary material in use. Tile profiles fall into two categories, plain and interlocking. The former simply lay one on top of another, like slates. Interlocking tiles are keyed into one another on either side.

Glass

Glass also originates from rock. It is manufactured from ground rock (soda-lime-silica). The most common type of glass is flat glass. This type is manufactured as clear float glass, patterned glass and wired glass. Tinted and

other surface treatments are applied to flo
special applications, such as solar controlled

Glass has very little thermal capacity but has a high
resistance to moisture. Because of this, windows are
particular targets of condensation. The glass is at virtually the same temperature as the outside air and the
surface is an impermeable vapour barrier. Run-off from
window condensation is a common cause of defects to
window frames of both metal and timber.

Since June 1992, there have been statutory requirements in the use of glass, extending the need to use
safety glass for areas of risk. In particular, these are
glazed doors, low-level glazing, side panels of doors,
and bathing screens. Many older properties have glazing which does not comply with these requirements.
When reglazing the present standards should be
achieved wherever possible in the interests of safety.

Where glass forms part of a fire separating wall, e.g.
between rooms, the glass is required to be wired or
otherwise fire-resistant. The size of panes is restricted
so that the fire integrity of the wall is not compromised.

Metal

Metals are used for external protection (e.g. roofs and
flashings), structural supports and for pipes, gutters,
cables, etc. External protection is commonly of lead or
zinc and occasionally of copper. All of these materials
will be found as coverings of roofs and as flashings at
junctions between roofs and surrounding walls.

Metals have a high propensity to move with temperature variations. Correct installation of metals therefore

requires allowance for such movement. The construction of movement joints and the separation of large areas into bays which can move independently of each other is essential. Rigid joints, such as soldered joints in zinc, will have a tendency to fail or cause buckling and failure of the metal itself if there is insufficient allowance for thermal movement.

Structural metalwork, e.g. steel beams, is factory made and assembled on site. Joints are formed either by welding, or by bolted or rivetted connections. For protection against both corrosion and fire, structural steel is often encased in concrete. Where the steel does not require corrosion protection, e.g. over an opening in an internal wall, fire protection can be achieved by plaster or other fire-resistant cladding.

Asphalt, felt and other bituminous materials

Asphalt is used as a covering to flat or shallow pitched roofs. It is applied in heated form as a liquid and, once cooled, forms an impervious surface. Sand is rubbed into the surface to minimise the effect of the surface being coated with a layer of its bitumen constituent, which will tend to craze. Solar reflective paints are often applied to asphalt to minimise temperature variations and oxidisation due to ultra violet radiation.

Roofing felt is a bituminous material bound together with mineral or synthetic fibres to form a sheet. It comes in rolls and is laid in either cold or hot compound over the roof structure. Although today some roofing felts are designed as single layer coverings, the majority are laid in three layers, bedded in hot bitumen to form a single composite covering.

As with asphalt, solar reflection assists in preserving the integrity of the roof covering and this is achieved either by chippings, a top layer of mineralised felt (i.e. small chippings embedded in felt) or solar reflective paint.

For both these materials, which are laid as impervious coverings, release of entrapped moisture or of vapour generated from below should be provided by pressure release vents. These look rather like plastic mushrooms over a roof surface.

Both asphalt and felt are used for damp-proofing courses and generally perform well. However, as both become brittle with age, they are susceptible to fail where any structural movement occurs.

CHAPTER 3

ENEMIES OF HEALTHY BUILDINGS

Water / *Dampness from the ground* / *Above ground* / *From above* / *From inside* / *From construction* / **Sulphates** / **Fungi** / *Dry rot* / *Wet rot* / *Moulds* / **Insects** / *Wood boring* / *Disease carrying* / *Just unpleasant* / **Metals** / **Hazardous materials** / *Asbestos* / *Glass fibre* / *Urea-formaldehyde foam* / *Radon gas* / **Users** / *Moisture generation* / **Animals** / *Disease carrying* / **Refuse** / **Plants, trees and bushes** / **Temperature and climate** / *Drought* / *Frost* / *Snow* / *Sun* / **Underground threats** / **Non-traditional buildings** / *Prefabricated buildings* / *Large panel systems* / *High rise* / *Modern timber-framed buildings*

If the materials from which we constructed our buildings were not largely inert then the adverse effects of the elements would be unlimited. Buildings would be eroded by rain, blown down by wind, overloaded by snow, overheated by the sun. These phenomena do take their toll on our buildings but, in general, building engineering has reduced these risks to a minimum.

Housing managers are unlikely to be faced with houses washed away by floods or in a state of near-collapse as a result of excessive winds, particularly in the UK. They are, however, going to face the more insidious degradation of the buildings.

Of all the defects likely to be encountered, dampness is the most common and potentially the most harmful, both to the structure and its occupants.

Water

Water can be an enemy of buildings in three ways:

First, water affects the structural stability of buildings by varying the supporting qualities of the sub-soil. Foundations are affected by water. When buildings are constructed, foundations are designed so that, except in extreme weather conditions, they will be unaffected by temperature or moisture content. Older houses will have shallow foundations and are more susceptible to seasonal movement.

Secondly, and perhaps more commonly, it provokes unwelcome life. The source of life out in the garden is also the source of life within the dwelling. When water comes into contact with any organic material it will provoke life. It will also attract and sustain life.

Thirdly, when an inorganic material, such as brick, plaster or concrete becomes wet, chemical changes occur. Carbon dioxide and sulphur dioxide are present in the air. When combined with water, these can convert to harmful acids which will attack stone and concrete as well as brickwork.

The identification of the source(s) of the water is

essential to specify the remedies, but, whatever the source, its effect can be the same. This is often forgotten when statements such as "It's not damp, it is only condensation" are made.

Moisture will pass through the structure by capillary action and direct flow. It will penetrate brickwork and concrete and will be halted only by an impervious barrier.

Damage from water does not occur only when there is a flood. Continuous, and even intermittent, dampness will also cause defects and is, in the UK, the most common source of building defects.

Appendix II helps the identification of sources of dampness.

Dampness from the ground

Rising damp

Even in a drought the ground takes a long time to dry out. The water level and content in the soil may vary and, as seen elsewhere, this may cause structural problems but the soil will still be damp and capable of transmitting that dampness to the building above.

Rising damp was the primary source of dampness in buildings in the last century. It was this defect which succeeding Public Health Acts and Building Acts sought to remedy along with insanitary drainage and washing facilities. It has not been cured over a century later.

Rising damp can be confused with other sources of dampness. It has become the common name for all dampness originating out of the soil. However, its true meaning is only the moisture rising vertically within a wall or through a floor. This distinction is important when identifying the source of and liability for a defect.

In modern housing, impervious barriers to rising damp are unlikely to fail if correctly installed. Failure of older damp-proof courses, such as slate, bitumen or asphalt, is likely due to the deterioration of the material. Where structural movement occurs this may provoke rising damp due to fracture of the membrane.

Remedial treatments such as silicone injection can be successful. However, the design and installation of these remedial treatments depends not just on the injection itself but on a whole series of other factors. It is the failure to deal with these other factors which is the primary cause of recurrent rising damp.

The narrow definition of rising damp was made earlier. This is particularly relevant where remedial works have been carried out and where dampness re-curs. In most cases, an injection damp-proof course will be covered by a guarantee. However, the guarantee rarely covers the recurrence of damp. What it warrants is that the damp-proof course injection will not fail. Therefore, when dampness recurs but the injected barrier is still working, there will be no claim on the damp-proof installation.

It is with this in mind that other sources of damp-ness, associated with rising damp but not actually rising through the structure, must be considered.

Lateral penetration

Lateral penetration does not only mean horizontal. Penetration of moisture through a wall or floor may occur where the damp-proofing is working but is being by-passed.

Where external ground level is above or close to the damp-proof course, moisture will pass across or around the impervious layer.

Rooms below ground level are particularly vulnerable to lateral penetration as the external walls will be earth-retaining. The walls of older properties will be protected externally with similar materials to those used for a horizontal damp-proof course.

Modern basements are constructed with an impervious membrane on the exterior of the wall linked through to the floor to provide a complete tank, rather like a swimming pool, but with the water only on the outside. The floor and walls support the membrane, and the load from the ground holds it in a sandwich between the structure and the soil.

In old basements, or any buildings where the floor is below external ground level, remedial works can be successful only if they replicate this modern construction. This does not require demolition and rebuilding or excavation around the perimeter. It does require the sealing of the walls to the floor and the application of material to the walls which will withstand the hydrostatic pressure from the ground water. This remedial treatment, known as "tanking", is common but nonetheless problematic.

Remedial damp-proofing
Remedial treatments to older buildings are generally carried out by specialists. The level of expertise will, however, vary considerably, and the acceptance of responsibility for recurrence of dampness can be very difficult to achieve. Virtually all remedial treatments work well in the laboratory. The problems start when they are applied to real buildings by people.

The repair of dampness from the ground depends

totally for its success on the condition of the base which is to be treated. Old walls often contain voids into which the injected silicone can flow, not forming a complete horizontal barrier in the masonry. Broken brickwork in walls will not accept a silicone injection, neither will perished and friable bricks provide a stable base onto which cement tanking can be applied. Floors need to be stable and of adequate strength to accept a damp-proof membrane. If the base on which the repair is applied fails, then the repair itself will fail.

Bridging

Solid floors at or below ground level should contain a damp-proof membrane to resist the moisture from the ground. To provide a comprehensive barrier to dampness, this membrane must link to the damp-proof course treatment of the enclosing walls.

In cases of recurrent dampness in older properties, a common failure is not with the injected damp-proof course, or with the floor membrane, but is the link between the two. The reason for this is that although the wall is treated by a specialist, the floor membrane is laid by largely unskilled labour as part of the placing of the concrete forming the floor structure. A little extra care at this stage would save thousands, if not millions of pounds across the UK.

Where the membrane has been covered by the concrete of the floor and not turned up at the wall abutments, the junction between the concrete and the wall will form a ready route for moisture.

Similarly, plaster internally or render externally which covers the damp-proof course will allow bridging, i.e. capillary action taking moisture past the damp-proof course.

esidual dampness

moisture from the ground contains salts. It is the presence of these salts which assists in the identification of the source(s) of dampness (see Appendix II). When repairs are carried out, the salts will remain in the masonry. Unless the plaster internally contains an additive to act as a salt-inhibitor, these salts will migrate to the interior and cause staining and damage to decorations. The salts will also contaminate the plaster and absorb moisture from the atmosphere, resulting in recurrent dampness.

Treatment of a damp wall does not make it dry immediately. As a rough guide, the wall will dry out at the rate of 1 month for each 25mm (1″) of thickness. On this basis a one-brick thick solid wall will take nine months to dry out.

Where possible, the building, should be left unoccupied and gently dried out. In the real world this is rarely possible. The replastering after a remedial damp-proof course has been inserted has to resist the migration of this residual dampness to the interior.

This in itself will slow the drying process as the moisture will then primarily dry externally. However, by applying the correct mix of plaster, some moisture discharge is possible internally without causing undue discomfort or damage. It is for this reason that following damp-proofing work, only water-based, not vinyl, emulsion paint should be applied to the walls until the drying out is completed. Under no circumstances should impermeable wallcoverings be applied for at least 12 months after treatment.

Dampness from the ground can therefore be due to:

• absence of an effective barrier to rising damp and/or;

• absence of an effective link between the wall damp-proof course and the damp-proof membrane to the floor, and/or;

• the bridging of the wall damp-proof course by render externally or plaster internally, and/or;

• the migration of salts from the treated wall through an inappropriate plaster mix to the interior, and/or;

• residual moisture in the structure.

Appendix II will assist you in narrowing down these possibilities, but do not be tempted to eliminate any of them until you are 100 per cent sure that it cannot apply.

Above ground

"Above ground" in this context means above the damp-proofing layer. It therefore includes the lowest floor.

In building work today, pipework is rarely run in a concrete floor. This is because the pipes are generally of copper which will corrode if unprotected in cement. The corrosion will perforate the copper, leading to leaks. Unfortunately, the majority of buildings built up to about 1980 will have pipes buried in the floors.

When pipes leak, water is discharged and causes damage. Weeping pipes, connections and fittings can cause substantial damage over a period of time, even though the leakage may be intermittent or at a low rate.

Plumbers are increasingly asked to fit washing machines and dishwashers which are built-in or partly concealed by worktops, cupboards, etc. As the pipework is concealed these appliances may need checking to find the source of the leak.

From above

When water enters at one point, it will not usually flow directly down to the interior. Below the external covering is a whole series of layers which will each absorb the water before it passes to the next layer down and eventually to the interior. Water will find the easiest route and, even if it has penetrated directly to the upper surface of a ceiling, it will look for cracks and joints in the plaster to pass through to the room below.

A very small failure in the covering can give rise to significant water penetration. Once water has entered, it can have the same effects of vapour build-up and deterioration of the structure as water from any other source.

Cavity construction for walls

Cavity walls have a special requirement for damp-proofing. It is part of their design that water can enter the outer layer but will not penetrate to the interior. Around openings and wherever the cavity is bridged, by a floor beam for example, then a damp-proof membrane has to be installed.

As with so many parts of the building process, quantity gives precedence to quality and these damp-proofing measures were often omitted or installed inadequately. Remedial works can be expensive and disruptive.

Where insulation is installed in the cavity, the choice of materials and the installation must ensure that a bridge is not provided to allow external moisture to penetrate to the inner surface. The materials used in new work are fixed so that an air gap remains between the outer face of the insulation and the inner face of the external skin. For remedial insulation systems, the use of moisture-resistant and largely impervious materials minimises the risk of water transmission (Appendix I – fig. 1.2).

From inside

Condensation

Air contains water held in vapour form. The hotter the air, the more water vapour it can hold. The quantity of vapour in the air is measured as Relative Humidity. There is no inherent problem with this moisture until the air meets a colder and impervious surface. The air is cooled and can hold less water. The excess water condenses out onto the colder and impervious surface and forms water droplets. The water from this source has less salts in it than water from the ground, but it can cause an equal amount of damage to buildings.

The balance between heating, ventilation and insulation will need to be right to overcome this problem. It will be affected by moisture generation, but the basic failings of the building have to be present for any except the most extremely unreasonable usage to cause severe problems. The adjustment of any of the three factors will modify and may ameliorate the conditions, but it is only the balancing of all three that will cure the problem.

Relative humidity levels of around 50 to 60 per cent should not produce excess dampness and will maintain an adequate comfort level without excessive dryness. However, if humidity levels increase to 70 per cent or more then condensation will be commonplace and will sustain and generate the moulds and insect infestations referred to later.

Interstitial condensation

This is condensation occurring within part of the building structure, commonly in roofs. Water vapour entering a flat roof structure struggles to escape or else condenses on the underside of a colder, impervious layer (usually the underside of the roof covering). This has two effects. First, it will cause the structure of the roof to become damp with all the consequences following as described. Secondly, the build-up of vapour in the roof will expose any weakness in adhesion of the roof covering, causing it to bubble upwards.

From construction

Vast quantities of water are used in construction. Most of the materials used in buildings either contain water or are mixed using water. All of this moisture has to dry out and be removed from the building.

Sulphates

Brickwork is vulnerable to chemical attack. Sulphates from rainwater or from constituent parts of the building will react with Portland Cement (a primary constituent of mortar). This reaction causes the expansion of the sulphate, in turn causing expansion of the brickwork. Where cavity brickwork is used, or where solid walls are constructed of different quality bricks for the inside and outside, this expansion can cause distortion of the wall.

Gases in flues can often cause sulphate attack to the chimney, at which level the flue is not lined and the gases condense out on the inside face of the bricks.

Fungi

Fungal decay attacks all organic materials not just timber. Fungi are plants and grow and reproduce. Their spores (seeds) are in the air and will germinate wherever there is an inviting host.

In buildings, we are concerned with those fungi which live off dead material. The identification of broad categories of fungal decay is necessary as the consequences of their action and the repairs required will vary widely.

Dry rot

Dry rot *(Serpula Lacrymans)* is a fungus which has remarkable powers of survival. Thought to originate in the Himalayas, it is perhaps a by-product of Britain's imperial past.

As with other wood-rotting fungi, it requires a moisture content of dead timber in excess of 19 per cent to start germination. What distinguishes it from other fungi, however, is its ability to survive and grow even when that moisture level is reduced. Dry rot will be able to survive in timber with a moisture content of 14 per cent. On the other hand where the moisture content is 40 per cent or more, it is unlikely to grow.

This ability to spread in relatively dry conditions, and to continue spreading after a water source is removed, makes it the most difficult to treat. Treatment will have to extend to at least 1m beyond the last growth and will include removal of all organic material. In older dwellings, this will include plaster which contains animal hair or other organic material as a binding agent.

Dry rot is able to travel through brickwork, finding

passages in mortar joints and feeding off the hair and other organic material. It will attack furniture and belongings and can remain concealed until finally manifesting itself when it is too late.

When visible, its first characteristic is warping or wrinkling of the wood, with often the outer, exposed surface remaining intact while the material behind decays. The decaying material affected by dry rot has a cuboid cracking pattern, both along and across the grain of the timber. This cuboid pattern is also found with some wet rot fungi (see below), but in all cases erring on the side of caution is recommended: where such patterns are found, dry rot must be suspected.

In advanced stages, and only in concealed areas, mycelium in white/cream sheets with tentacles will be found on the surface of the affected material. When threatened, the fungus seeks to reproduce and creates a fruiting body. These can be really beautiful. They are flat, slightly puffy growths with white perimeter and rust red centres. The red part is the spore bank from which the spores are spread by air movements to new feeding grounds.

Wet rot

Wet rot fungi, of which there are thousands, if not millions, require high moisture levels to survive, usually in excess of 40 per cent. Once the water source has been cut off, the fungus dies.

The manifestation of fungal decay by wet rot fungi has a common thread, the distortion of the affected surface of the timber and disintegration of the material. In most cases, there is also a dark staining which is a useful, but not 100 per cent certain, guide to distinguishing a wet rot attack from dry rot. The affected timber will still be damp if the attack is active.

Remedial treatment is therefore limited to replacement of unsound material and chemical treatment of the affected areas. The chemical treatment must be carried out. However, it is common for a wet rot attack to be cured by cutting off the water source only to find that dry rot takes over as soon as the moisture content declines.

Moulds

Many of the moulds found in dwellings are allergenic. Moulds require moisture (some more than 65 per cent moisture content), moderate temperatures (13-15°C) and suitable food. The food source is commonly wallpaper paste, but may also be clothing and belongings.

The allergic reaction of the occupants will depend on the toxicity, buoyancy and concentration of the allergen. The most effective way to control mould spore allergens is by reducing moisture levels in the air. Increased ventilation can relieve these problems, but it has to be balanced against temperature levels and the ability to maintain heat levels.

Insects

Wood-boring

Wood-boring insects attack dead wood. Their presence is identified by their flight holes, usually small in diameter. It is the weakening of the timber by these holes and the internal passage cut out by the insects as food which cause the damage.

Detection in advance of some damage is difficult, if not impossible. The insects are minute, often not readily visible to the naked eye. The only manifestation of their presence is the flight hole after they have gone and a small pile of frass (digested and excreted wood dust) left behind, around and below the flight hole.

A tell-tale sign of death-watch beetle, which attacks oak, is the knocking sound it makes. It is unlikely that many housing managers will be involved in buildings using oak, and even less likely that they would be able to stay there in silence to hear the tapping sound. However, if buildings contain oak, an occupant's complaints about tapping sounds in the middle of the night should not be dismissed as irrelevant to disrepair.

These insects have a seasonal life-cycle. The emerging insects lay eggs on the surface or within the wood. The egg germinates and the grub begins its life within the timber. The grub feeds off the wood and, after metamorphosis into the flying beetle, emerges by eating its way through to the exterior.

Some, such as death-watch beetle, do not emerge every year, but the presence of flight holes, especially if frass is visible, indicates that the infestation is active. Remedial treatment is required to prevent the subsequent generations from boring more holes and causing damage. Treatment against common insects is now almost routine in rehabilitation work. In new buildings, pre-treated timber is normally used.

Disease carrying

Cockroaches have developed a survival rate which has to be admired. They can move from one dwelling and contaminate another while the first is treated and then re-occupy the first when safe to do so. For this reason treatment of individual dwellings in a block of flats is unlikely to be successful. Whole block treatments are the only hope. Many local authorities have rolling pro-grammes of whole block treatments which require rep-etition at frequent intervals to overcome this infestation.

Ants will also occupy homes, feeding off foodstuffs. They prefer damp, dirty and unhygienic food stores, but, as with cockroaches, will require whole building treatment to eradicate them.

Fleas (both human and animal) can usually be treated effectively, but their removal will require the source to be treated also (e.g. the pet).

House mites are a major source of allergens. They are barely visible to the naked eye and are usually found in house dust and in bedding. The mites feed on dead human skin. They require a high humidity level of not less than 45 per cent and therefore damp conditions increase their population and activity.

Just unpleasant

Silverfish, wood lice and other harmless insects are inconvenient and unpleasant but do not carry disease or provoke allergic reactions.

Metals

Metals will corrode when affected by water, but this is not just the effect of the water. Metals are affected by electrolitic action, and this occurs when two different metals are linked by a conducting medium such as water. In buildings the most common metals which adversely react together are zinc and copper. Zinc is used not just in its own right, but as the galvanised coating to steel. Galvanised water pipes and water tanks joined to copper pipes will corrode.

Hazardous materials

Asbestos

Although the use of asbestos in new buildings is now almost non-existent it needs to be removed from older properties. Asbestos is used in various forms and there are three distinct types, shown in the table below together with details about its use and removal.

Asbestos-based materials	Where used	How to strip out
Asbestos-cement boarding	Commonly used as roofing material, water tanks, flue pipes, etc. Contains about 10 to 15% Chrysotile and 85 to 90% Portland Cement, mixed with water. Flue pipes may contain Amosite.	Wet stripping may be permissible if there is no prospect of breakage or fracturing, but where this is not guaranteed, then an enclosure should be provided.
Insulation board	Commonly used as fire-resisting board. Contains up to 40% Amosite or Amosite mixed with Chrysotile with 60 to 84% calcium silicate.	Stripping can be carried out only using enclosures.
Rope and gaskets	Commonly used to seal flexible joints. Can contain over 90% asbestos, usually Chrysotile or Crocidolite.	Stripping can be carried out only using enclosures

Removal contractors

Since 1 August 1984, all asbestos removal contractors must be licensed by the Health and Safety Executive under the Asbestos (Licensing) Regulations 1983. The Asbestos Removal Contractors Association is a trade association which promotes high standards. Contractors, including self-employed operatives, should be members of the association and licensed by the Health and Safety Executive.

Glass fibre

Glass fibre wool is used in buildings as an insulant, usually as a matting. It will be found in lofts, where it is laid over the ceiling or under the roof, and in cavity and timber walls, all to reduce heat loss. It is used for pipe and tank lagging and in a denser form as sound insulation quilt.

Glass fibre wool has raised similar concerns to asbestos in the past but is not considered to be anything like as hazardous. A recent report concluded that it was not a significant health hazard. Nevertheless, strands will cause irritation to the skin and to breathing and suitable precautions should be taken when handling.

Urea-formaldehyde foam

Urea-formaldehyde foam when mixed will release formaldehyde. At low concentrations this will irritate the eyes and cause nausea and some breathing difficulties. It is used as an insulating material in cavity walls into which it can be pumped.

Radon gas

Radon gas is the result of the breakdown of uranium 238. The gas seeps out of the ground and will enter buildings. Increased insulation and restricted ventilation has resulted in a higher risk to occupants of dwellings.

Concentrations vary throughout the UK but where high, increased incidences of lung cancer have been reported.

Users

Buildings would operate perfectly well if no one occupied them. This may seem to be a ridiculous statement but we cause no end of problems when we start to live in these structures. In particular, we cause dampness.

Moisture generation

We all generate moisture by breathing, washing ourselves and our clothes, cooking and heating. For example, four people in a house for 12 hours will generate 2.5kg of moisture. Cooking and food preparation can produce 3.7kg per day, floor mopping 1.1kg, clothes drying 12kg and clothes washing 2kg. The construction and design of the dwelling should overcome the generation of these relatively large amounts of water by balancing insulation, ventilation and heating.

The use of flueless gas heaters (e.g. calor gas) and paraffin heaters creates further water vapour. For example, a paraffin heater will discharge 1 litre of water vapour into the air for each litre of oil burned.

Sweating also generates moisture. Although we expect sweating to occur at higher temperatures, it must be remembered that this is related to humidity levels as well as temperature. For example, at a humidity level of 22 per cent, profuse sweating does not occur until 30°C, but at a humidity of 60 per cent it will occur at 20 to 25°C.

Animals

Disease carrying

Pets, the great love of the British, are a primary source of fleas in our homes.

Disposal of faeces from pets is also a real problem, especially in blocks of flats. The effects of dog faeces on health have been well publicised and proper hygienic cleansing of areas used for defecating by pets must be maintained.

Rats and mice are probably the most common invaders. Rodents carry many diseases; mainly in the parasitic fleas which live on their bodies. They will, if cornered, attack humans and care must be taken in entering cellars or sewers where rats are likely to be present.

Refuse

We produce refuse which we fail to dispose of properly, or even to seal up pending disposal. We flush our waste down the drains, but how often do we clean out those same drains?

Plants, trees and bushes

Although we see plants as growing where we plant them in our gardens or window boxes, they have a life of their own. The seeds are in the air and will propagate wherever there is a source of food and water. They do not exclude parts of our buildings from this. In some instances, plant growth will be as a result of poor building maintenance. Where pointing to brickwork has been eroded, plants will often take root. In other instances, domestic plants will expand beyond the confines of the plant pot and, particularly with creepers, seek out walls over which to climb.

Plant-covered walls can be attractive to look at but with few exceptions they will conceal the damage being caused to the fabric of the building. Plants need water and will obtain it from any source. The roots which are produced to search for and absorb the moisture will be capable of finding a way through minimal openings, even between bricks. As these roots develop, they expand. The expansion will widen the gaps between the building elements, allowing more water to enter and setting in train a cycle of deterioration.

Trees and bushes also have adverse effects on buildings, but primarily external. In the hot summers of 1976 and 1995, buildings cracked. As will be seen below, the moisture in the soil, affected by drought or flood, will have a damaging effect on buildings. Trees and bushes need water to survive and in times of drought root growth will extend in search of water. The extraction of the limited moisture from the soil will cause further damage.

Temperature and climate

Drought

The main effect is on the sub-soil and on the foundations, but high temperature levels also cause unusual thermal movement of the building elements putting unexpected strain on the joints and junctions.

In times of drought, e.g. 1976 and 1995, sub-soils such as clay shrink. Voids are created causing compression and slipping of the clay layers. This removes support from foundations of buildings. The subsequent cracking of buildings is known as settlement.

As noted above, this drying out of the sub-soil will be hastened by trees and bushes extracting the remaining moisture. Often, therefore, serious settlement problems are a combination of changing sub-soil conditions and root growth.

Frost

Frost mainly affects the exposed surfaces of the building. Water expands when frozen. If water has entered the building fabric and then freezes, the expansion will cause damage, splitting bricks, breaking concrete. The opening thus created lets in more moisture, continuing the cycle at an accelerated rate.

When tanks and pipes are not lagged, freezing will open joints and split pipes. When the temperature rises, the water flows.

Snow

Snow imposes significantly increased loads on roofs. Modern roofs are designed for normal snow loads, but in exceptional conditions structural failure is possible. Snow will also pull slates and tiles down roof slopes.

Rainwater pipes blocked with snow will not be able to carry away the water discharging from the roof when the thaw starts. There will be a time delay between the warming of the roof and the thawing of the ice in the pipe. During this period overflowing and leakage should be expected.

Sun

The sun discharges heat and radiation. The heat has a direct effect on buildings by causing expansion of materials, which in turn will cause fracturing of the less flexible elements. Ultra-violet radiation from the sun will cause oxidisation of asphalt and break down the surface. Temperature changes will affect some materials more than others.

Underground threats

In mining, quarry or other areas where extraction industries are, or were, there is a risk of sub-soil movement. This occurs due to the soil falling into the voids left after extraction and is known as subsidence. The effect on buildings is very similar to settlement, but it is a distinct cause. The difference is important not just in the remedial works required, but in the securing of insurance and the possibility of recovery of costs of remedial work.

The effects of underground streams is often forgotten, particularly when there is a propensity to settlement, e.g in clay sub-soils. Water courses will erode sub-soils giving rise to subsidence. Water will find the easiest route. When desiccation of the sub-soil occurs, either through drought or water extraction, the streams may well change course. This, in turn, can give rise to problems of flooding and erosion of sub-soil in an otherwise unaffected location.

Non-traditional buildings

Buildings are unpredictable. Traditional buildings will not all fail in the same way, or at the same time. Similarly, with non-traditional buildings, failures will depend on the same multitude of factors with similar scope for variation.

Prefabricated buildings

The Housing Defects Act 1984 (now Housing Act 1985, Part XVI) designated certain types of prefabricated dwellings which were known to be vulnerable to major structural deterioration. The Act defined the types and through accompanying information papers gave details of the construction and vulnerability. All of these types were of reinforced concrete construction. Other prefabricated buildings were constructed in the inter-war and immediately post-war years, including many steel-framed designs. The British Iron and Steel Federation (BISF) houses were manufactured in substantial quantities and can be found throughout the UK. The designs and potential defects in these buildings can be found in BRE publications

Large panel systems

These were used extensively in the UK during the 1960s housing boom. They were manufactured by individual companies and sold as a kit, assembled on site. Although the designs worked beautifully on the drawing board, the designers had reckoned without the workforce. A combination of unskilled labour and a zeal for quantity rather than quality, lead inevitably to substantial construction defects. Perhaps the most notorious was Ronan Point which partially collapsed, but others have been more of a financial liability for their owners. Often the repair costs have been so high that demolition and rebuilding has been the only sensible solution.

The main sources of defects were the joints between panels. These were either not properly linked structurally, or were not adequately sealed against the weather.

The enemies of these buildings are in many ways the same as for traditional buildings, but the pack of cards structure means that localised failures can have a devastating effect on the whole structure.

High rise

Apart from the human and social costs of the 1960s adventure, high rise buildings pose special constructional problems. These apply whether the structure is of steel, reinforced concrete or prefabricated construction and are primarily linked to the height and exposure of the building.

The propensity for water penetration is always governed by the exposure of a building. High rise is clearly more exposed to wind and rain. The building is most vulnerable at construction joints and around openings. Windows originally installed were often of low quality, acceptable for low rise, but not sufficiently sealed for high rise.

Further defects to which high rise blocks are vulnerable are the accumulation of common defects found in all buildings which together increase the effect. Ventilation to bathrooms and toilets will often be via a shared vent stack which may or may not be powered. If the stack becomes blocked, or vents leading into it are permanently open, exhaust from a unit low down in the block will discharge to upper units. There is a real danger of fire spreading through the ducts from one unit to another. The installation of fire checks at each floor level was often a casualty of the quantity versus quality battle.

Blockage of the above-ground drainage can exert massive pressures on the pipework, causing spectacular and horrible explosions of waste and sewage. Vacating units for repairs can be an organisational nightmare.

Modern timber-framed buildings

Timber-framed buildings are quicker and cheaper to erect than conventional brick. They can also provide higher levels of insulation and comfort than masonry. However, the primary element of construction is timber and this is affected adversely by moisture. Vapour barriers – impervious membranes – are fitted within the structure to protect the timber from moisture from the exterior. Insulation is fitted to maintain the timber at a higher temperature, closer to that of the interior, so that condensation does not occur on the inside face of the vapour barrier. It is the failure of the detailing of this insulation and vapour barrier that is the most common source of moisture penetration.

Although water leakage and infiltration from other sources has a damaging effect on all buildings, this can cause major structural weakening for timber-framed buildings. Therefore, whenever dampness occurs, the likely effect on the timber structure must be considered.

PART II

INSPECTING
DISREPAIR

CHAPTER 4

PREPARING FOR THE INSPECTION

Housing manager's role / **Starting
points** / *Occupied dwellings* / *Voids* /
Third parties / **Is inspection
necessary?** / *Recording information* /
Background information /
Address and identification code /
Type of property / *Size and location* /
Building type / *Occupants* / *Tenancy
agreement* / *Common parts* /
Equipment / *Basics* /
Moisture meter

Housing manager's role

This book is concerned not just with complaints by an
occupant but also with the need for the housing manager to be aware of what defects may exist which are
giving rise to that complaint. If the housing manager is
to be effective in the first reaction to and diagnosis of
defects, then he or she must think about the underlying
cause of the problem. This is not to say that every hous-

ing manager has to have the experience, training and skills of a qualified surveyor, but that he or she should have sufficient common sense and knowledge of buildings to direct a train of thought to eliminate, at the least, the more serious implications.

Surveyors, in conducting inspections of properties, are expected to "follow the trail". This term has arisen out of actions taken against surveyors who have allegedly failed to notice or report on defects. The surveyor is expected not just to see what is visible but to raise questions prompted by what is seen.

For example, where a timber ground floor slopes to one side, it is not sufficient for a surveyor carrying out an inspection for a prospective purchaser merely to report the slope. It is expected that the surveyor will also assess the likely cause of the sloping and advise on what risks that poses and the possible implications. Advice on further investigation or tests to refine the diagnosis is also required. After all, it is this very advice which the surveyor's skill and experience is being called upon to supply.

Whereas the further investigation and analysis of data to identify conclusively an underlying defect may be beyond the skills required of housing managers, the identification of a trail to follow should be within their experience. Having identified that a trail or trails exist, it may well be necessary to hand the further investigation and interpretation over to a surveyor, architect or engineer colleague, or outside consultant. The housing manager must therefore be aware of where trails can start and be able to identify when other skills are required to assist diagnosis (see also chapters 7 and 9).

Example

Some 20 years ago a local councillor asked the author to advise a group of residents involved in a consultation exercise for an estate improvement scheme. The buildings were pre-1939 blocks of flats originally fitted with solid fuel fires, but these had been replaced with gas fires during the 1960s. There was no heating in the rooms other than the living room. The landlord (in this case the local authority) had based its assessment of priorities on the complaints received from tenants over the past five to ten years. The most common complaint had been about kitchen units. These had been installed in the 1960s and were, without exception, of laminate covered chipboard. They had disintegrated, as chipboard does when it gets wet.

The presentation to the residents was done on the basis that the highest priority was to replace these units. The residents were arguing for higher quality units, of solid timber rather than particle board, and the whole process was getting bogged down.

The authority had not consulted its professional advisers at this stage but had identified the cause of failure of the units as dampness. It had failed to look beyond this to see where the dampness originated, which in this case was condensation. Remedial work to minimise this condensation-caused dampness was required, but for some reason no one had interpreted the original complaints from tenants in that way.

To replace the units and not address the underlying cause would have been a waste of public money and a source of further dissatisfaction among the tenants.

Starting points

Occupied dwellings
With occupied dwellings, the most likely reason for instigating action is a complaint from the occupant. This may be by telephone, in person or in writing.

Voids
It may be that the housing manager is not dealing with an occupied dwelling but looking at a void property prior to allocation for letting. In this case, there is little to base the inspection on and a potentially wider range of defects may be encountered.

Third parties
The information may come from a third party such as a neighbour. For example, it may be that the leaking gutter has not yet been noticed by the tenant, but the consequent dampness is affecting the adjoining house.

Whichever of these is the starting point, the information required is the same. The checklist of questions which follows may seem obvious, but it is so easy to omit an essential element which may seem peripheral until later in the process.

Is inspection necessary?

Finite resources mean that not all complaints can, or should, be inspected by the manager. Every time a manager inspects, the money expended on that inspection is not being spent on a repair.

In some areas, e.g. London Borough of Croydon, tenants are supplied with a manual which enables them to discuss and identify the defect with the assistance and prompting of specially trained staff in the housing department. This empowerment of tenants not only reduces the need for the landlord to inspect before ordering repairs, but also gives the tenants a direct involvement in the repairs process.

Increasingly, landlords are ordering repairs directly on complaint and relying on completion notes from the tenant to validate the contractor's claim for payment. This is a tempting area for future cost-cutting and on the face of it performance of a repairs service may not be harmed. After all, in assessing whether inspections are required, the landlord, particularly a large local authority or association, must assess the cost of failure. If this can be shown to be only marginally worse when fewer inspections are carried out, there may be little financial justification for carrying out such inspections.

The decision to inspect must, therefore, be based on the benefit of such an inspection. This, in turn, can only be based on the information available at the initial complaint stage. This information must then be interpreted by the housing manager on the basis of risk. This risk assessment will take into account the data and the potential for escalating costs and liabilities if the problem is not accurately diagnosed.

Recording information

Methodical recording of all events, even if this is in some code or in note form, is an essential discipline. It cannot be emphasised too often how so many future disputes and difficulties of evidence arise out of a failure to take notes. It is very easy to rely on an over-pressured memory, to assume that all will be solved swiftly and without dispute, and that there will be no difference of recollection. All the processes and actions of the housing manager must be tempered by the possibility of a potential dispute at a later date. See further A. Kilpatrick *Repairs and Maintenance,* Arden's Housing Library vol. 5, 1996, on legal liability for disrepair.

Computer databases are increasingly used and are extremely useful tools, reducing paperwork and providing better access and potential for automatic filtering and initial diagnosis. They are, however, tools, not solutions, and the output is only as good as the input. Design and operation of any computer system need sufficient checks and balances to ensure that the housing manager is provided with the relevant information.

Recording the initial information
Recording of the complaint in a methodical way is essential. Cards and standard forms are used by many social housing landlords, recording as a minimum the following information:

• date and time information received;

• the name and address of the informant, with telephone number if there is one;

• the exact words used by the informant;

• any further information elicited by discussion of the problem.

This establishes the foundation from which the housing manager will build the response and, in particular, should provide sufficient information to decide whether an inspection is required after considering the background and recorded history available.

Background information

Before setting off on an inspection some basic information and equipment must be assembled. The information will start with the record of the information referred to above but will need to be expanded. Without these background data, the visit will be less productive and possibly inconclusive, requiring a second visit. Repeat visits to look at the same problem should be avoided. The costs to the landlord are largely wasted and the irritation to the complainant, who sees only visits and no action, is increased.

Address and identification code

This is needed not just to find the location of the property but also that records can be maintained and updated so that a clear picture can be constructed and retained over the years. Each landlord will have its own system of identification for recording the property history, often on an electronic database. This may be entered or sorted by address, postcode, dwelling type, tenant's name or rent roll reference. Whichever it is, a methodical and consistent recording of data and opinions is an essential requirement.

Where a housing manager is familiar with a specific area, that local knowledge and experience should also be brought into consideration. There is a risk of misdiagnosis of problems, especially if similar defects have apparently gone away in other properties. Therefore the knowledge must be weighed against the other sources of information to give a balanced view.

Type of property

This should identify whether it is a flat, a maisonette or a house. If it is a house, is it mid- or end-terrace, semi-detached or detached?

Size and location

A record should be kept of the number of habitable rooms and the number of storeys. If a flat, on which floors of what size of block? Is the block purpose-built or a conversion?

Building type

In the UK, there is a wide variety of building types, which are discussed in chapter 1. Is the building known to be a traditional structure with brick walls, timber windows, a tile or slate roof on a timber sloping structure and with timber floors? If not, what sort of structure is it?

This will be seen on inspection, but the landlord's records of type will allow some better pre-planning of the inspection. For example, if the building is of timber-framed construction, a defect such as a pipe leak which may on first glance seem minor could have a greater significance.

Occupants

Who is the tenant, how many people are in the house-hold and what are their ages? Are they in work? If a large, overcrowded – and impoverished – household is at home all day, this will have a significant effect on their use of the building. These social factors cannot be separated from housing, and disrepair is affected by them.

Tenancy agreement

What are the specific obligations of the landlord and tenant for this dwelling? (See A. Kilpatrick *Repairs and Maintenance*, ch. 2 pp. 16-19.) It is assumed that for the majority of lettings managed by housing staff the implied repairing obligations set out in section 11 of the Landlord and Tenant Act 1985 will apply (see A. Kilpatrick *Repairs and Maintenance*, ch. 2 pp. 11-16).

Common parts

The existence of common parts should be a constant caution because of the different ways in which the law treats these areas, even though from a lay point of view they may be indistinguishable in terms of the effect on both the building and the occupant (see A. Kilpatrick *Repairs and Maintenance*, ch. 2 pp. 22-24).

After consideration of all the background information the decision to inspect or not can be made. There is always the danger of preconceptions based on the existing repairs history, and of course the risk of repeating previously unsuccessful repairs based on inaccurate diagnoses.

There are no hard and fast rules which can be applied in all cases, but triggers based on the threats to the building, or the consequences for the occupants, should be used. Repeated reports of the same or similar defect should prompt questioning of why it has recurred.

Equipment

Basics

Having decided that an inspection is required, what equipment should be available and used? The equipment listed here may not be used on every visit but represents the minimum which should be carried on every inspection in case it is needed.

A *diary, clip-board, pen, pencil* and *paper* may sound obvious, but all too often we rely on an imperfect memory for dealing with work which we then fail to execute fully.

Although *tape recorders* for dictation of notes on site have clear advantages in terms of speed and volume of information, they should not entirely replace written notes. It is likely that some of the information you wish to record should be confidential, and the occupant could find it either puzzling or provocative. It is not always wise to enter into debate with the tenant before any diagnosis has been thought through. The failure of a machine to record, or erasure of the tape accidentally is another risk.

The perceived increased efficiency and speed of a tape recorder is a reality only where there are adequate support services available to transcribe the tape immediately on return to the office. The presence of background noise, either from the occupants, the television or from traffic, will blur the recording and make accurate transcription even harder.

There is no permanent record of what was seen, except for a typed transcript which could contain minor typographical errors significantly altering the record, e.g. the omission of the negative in describing the condition of a wall. The significance of contemporaneous notes is discussed later in chapter 9.

Hand-held computers are also available for site use. These can log the defect and the repair required. The information is later down-loaded and linked to the database and ordering systems. While successful at these tasks, they are less likely to record all the information collected on the inspection and will rarely record the diagnosis, which leads to the bald statement of what is wrong and what repair is required.

A good *torch* is essential. Even with occupied properties, there will be cupboards, dark corners and unlit areas where clues to defects could lurk. With empty properties, it is likely that there will be no electricity.

A small *screwdriver* or a *Swiss Army knife* is required to probe into wood and for scraping material, either to identify it or to take samples.

A *measuring tape* is a good idea, at least 5m (16′) in length, to take overall measurements of rooms where this may be a consideration.

A small *sealable container*, such as a 35mm film cassette or tough plastic bag is useful for carrying of samples such as insects or fungus for later identification.

Moisture meter

For any inspection where either there is a complaint of dampness or where there is no specific defect identified prior to the visit, for example on a re-let, an electric moisture meter, however basic, is required. This measures the electric current passing through the material being tested between two probes. The greater the conductivity of the material, the higher the reading on the scale.

There is commonly assumed to be a direct relationship between the conductivity and moisture content of the material, but this is not always the case. The diagnosis of dampness is dealt with in chapter 3 but it must always be remembered that a moisture meter is an aid to diagnosis, not the means of diagnosis itself.

Moisture meters commonly display readings by a Wood Moisture Equivalent number (WME). Of all the materials found in buildings, wood is one for which a per cent moisture content reading is meaningful: it is generally accepted that wood rots when it is wetter than 20 per cent and is safe below this level. This is why moisture meters have a scale for wood. In any material other than wood the meters will give readings of % Wood Moisture Equivalent (% WME). To put it another way: % WME is the moisture level in any building material other than wood expressed as a moisture content of wood. Therefore a reading above 20 per cent in any building material indicates a hazardous condition which must be investigated further.

Camera
Wherever possible, a photographic record of the inspection should be taken. This should supplement, not replace, the written notes. It is more important to have a photograph of the general condition and layout of the premises than a detailed close-up of a particular alleged defect (see also chapter 9).

CHAPTER 5

THE INSPECTION

**Appointments and casual call
systems /** *Diary systems* **/ Health and
safety / Making appointments /
Conducting the inspection /**
Introductions **/** *Preliminaries* **/
Methodical procedure /** *Using the
senses* **/** *Identifying defects* **/
Inspection notes / A practical
illustration / Timescales /
Do-It-Yourself**

The purpose of the inspection is to obtain information
which will be used for a variety of reports and actions.
It is an information gathering exercise, part of an
overall process. It is not an end in itself. There may be
limited opportunities to inspect for a variety of reasons,
such as the unwillingness of the occupier to give access,
the inability of the occupier to be at home because of
work or other commitments, etc. Repeat inspections to
get information which should be obtained on a single
visit are a waste of resources and a devaluation of
the process.

This chapter deals primarily with inspections of the vast majority of dwellings where the occupants are co-operative. However, there are also those cases where an occupant is known to be violent or where violence erupts during the inspection. These, thankfully relatively rare cases, are dealt with later in this chapter. Most landlords will have their own records of tenants likely to be violent.

The experience of predecessors and more experienced colleagues is an extremely important resource for the newly-arrived housing manager. Wherever possible, new managers should shadow or be inducted by colleagues whose greater experience can be passed on with much greater effect than the written word.

Appointments and casual call systems

Many landlords with large stocks to maintain rely on calling without an appointment, leaving a card inviting the occupant to contact for another appointment if there is no response. To the occupant, this may appear as a lack of respect, not taking the status and the privacy of the family seriously and reducing their timetable and needs to a level lower than that of the landlord's worker. This does not provide a co-operative climate in which to approach the visit and will almost without exception start a confrontational relationship which need not be there.

This system may in some cases appear to be an efficient use of resources, maximising staff time, but is it really? How many abortive calls are there for each successful call? What is the cost to the landlord of future confrontations aggravated by, if not borne out of, this casual approach to the tenants' needs?

Similar problems will result from a lack of punctuality. Unless the delay is unavoidable, tenants should not be kept waiting. After all, when the housing manager invites a tenant to meet at the office, the tenant is expected to arrive on time.

There is no coherent or sustainable arguments for bad time management and this, after all, is what the casual call system is. It is where the manager is unable to plan workload and time to maximise productivity in the working day. Good time management is essential and this requires that inspections are made by appointment.

Diary systems

The working systems of landlords will vary widely. A "patch" system where each housing manager, or even a team, works on a particular area of the housing stock is recognised as a basically good one. However, with increasing use of short-term contracts and agency personnel, landlords may not be able to operate this system; or even if they do, frequent changes in personnel negate the advantages which should be derived from it. Where a person or team is dedicated to a patch, it will, of course, be more difficult to provide for substitution and cover for absences.

With these caveats, there are several different mechanisms which can assist the office in achieving efficiency:

1. *A single centralised diary* for those carrying out visits/inspections. To be effective as a source for arranging appointments, such a diary needs to have time slots where people are available, not the times when they have appointments. Variations to the times have to be logged centrally with consequent restrictions on individuals arranging further inspections without reference back to the central control. This can therefore appear to provide control and efficiency, but in effect reduces the freedom and flexibility of the individual and makes them less efficient.

2. *Individual diaries with no central liaison* are perhaps the most common. The result is that only the operatives themselves can arrange any appointments, leaving their colleagues and their customers frustrated and disenchanted. Additionally, there is no office record of where such operatives have gone.

3. *Individual diaries linked and co-ordinated centrally* are a composite of systems 1 and 2, with a central diary containing the individual diaries of all workers, up-dated daily and with time slots within which individuals have the liberty to arrange appointments as they arise during the day. By enabling individuals to arrange appointments within an agreed space of time, it restores individual control over workload but maintains an overview of the work and appointments of the whole staff, enabling some swapping of tasks and visits to maximise resources. It requires dialogue between workers and a spirit of co-operation and team-building.

Health and safety

It is an essential health and safety requirement that the office knows where the on-site operatives have gone and when they are due to return, or attend at another property. Guidelines on the safety of inspectors or others visiting premises away from their office have been prepared by the Lamplugh Trust. (This trust was set up after the disappearance of estate agent Suzy Lamplugh, apparently while out of the office showing a prospective purchaser around a vacant house.) Throughout the inspection keep in mind the requirements of health and safety. There is no room for heroics, and climbing on chairs or other unsatisfactory access equipment to get a better view is an unacceptable risk.

Making appointments

Preferably all appointments should be either made or confirmed in writing. Even where the appointment is arranged initially by telephone, the time and date should be confirmed. Where a precise time is not possible, e.g. where a series of inspections of uncertain duration is anticipated, a time frame of not more than one hour for the time of arrival should be given.

How can this work in practice for a range of inspections, from urgent to optional? In an emergency, written appointments are not appropriate, the time being arranged orally, preferably when the call reporting the problem is received. This is achievable where a centralised record of individuals' commitments is maintained (as in system 3 above).

For all other appointments a letter, or a telephone call followed by a confirming letter, is essential. The letter generally suggests a time and date for the inspection but leaves unasked the questions of whether that time is acceptable and whether the tenant will be at home. This results in a vast waste of resources on the part of housing management staff. The use of pre-paid reply cards, confirming the acceptance of the offered time, is recommended. Non-receipt of the reply card confirming the appointment should always result in the appointment being cancelled and a further one offered.

Two problems arise in the use of such response-led appointments, namely the need for special consideration of tenants for whom English is not their first language and those with reading difficulties. Overcoming these problems and the potential cost of unused postage should not outweigh the benefits of pre-paid cards. Tenants' special needs will still have to be catered for.

The documentation of the appointment is complete if this process is followed. This may seem of little relevance, but should litigation result it could be of vital importance to demonstrate the landlord's response to a report by the tenant. (See A. Kilpatrick *Repairs and Maintenance,* ch. 2 p. 35 and Appendix I).

Conducting the inspection

The inspection will usually have been prompted by a complaint or report of a defect by the occupant. In most cases, this will potentially affect the interior of the dwelling, even if it is reported as an external defect only, e.g. a slipped roof slate. There will be the exceptions of course, such as the broken garden fence or other external defect which has no potential for affecting the interior or the structure of the dwelling. In these relatively rare cases, inspection of the interior may not be necessary, but in general a comprehensive inspection is essential.

Introductions

The management of housing includes the establishment of a working relationship between the manager and the tenants. Managers will be visiting tenants for a number of reasons, only one of which will be disrepair. Nevertheless, it is worthwhile remembering that you are visiting someone's home. If it is for the first time, treat it as you would a visit to your aunt's friend whom you have never met. You will usually be accepted and treated with as much respect as you show to the tenant. If you have visited previously, whatever the prior history, approach the home with respect and with candour.

It is often helpful to have a view of the neighbourhood and the adjoining houses before entering the particular property. There may be occasions when you are meeting with colleagues at the premises. The sight of a manager hovering outside is disconcerting. As soon as you arrive knock at the door to introduce yourself. Explain that you are having a brief look around the area, or are waiting for colleagues, and will call back shortly.

Preliminaries

Before commencing the inspection, an assessment of the character and type of adjoining premises, the general tone of the area and the age of the neighbourhood should be made. For managers operating a patch, or for those with current local knowledge, this will be familiar ground and will not need repeating. The environment in which the property is located will have significance in determining the possible causes of disrepair, the likelihood of defects recurring and the appropriate level and quality of repair required.

An initial assessment of the dwelling is useful. Is it

of a standard type, likely to manifest similar defects to others in the neighbourhood of which you already have some knowledge? When was it first constructed, and has it been substantially renovated or altered since? What is its likely life span before either demolition and redevelopment is required or major works of improvement and renovation are carried out? Again, managers operating a patch, or those with current local knowledge, should already have this information available.

The initial conversation with the tenant will inevitably contain much which is not directly relevant to the inspection, but issues such as late or inadequate benefit payments, high heating charges, recent family traumas or separations may all have an effect on the occupation of the dwelling or result from defects in the premises. Their relevance cannot be discounted but must be filtered.

Methodical procedure

The inspection must always be methodical. It can be difficult when an anxious occupier wants you to look at the kitchen, to insist on looking in the bedroom first. There needs to be a willingness to take a quick look at the problems presented by the tenant, coupled with an assurance that you need to inspect the whole property in order to have an overview not only of the defect reported, but also its effect on occupation. This establishes a rapport and conveys to the tenant that you are listening to what they have to say.

The tenant's perception of the repair history can often provide an insight into previous actions which cannot be gleaned from the landlord's records. It can often give vital clues showing that previous attempts at repair or diagnosis have overlooked the real cause of the problem. The experience of tenants is all-important; after all, they live in the property.

You must decide before you inspect how you will describe locations. Compass bearings can be used but can lead to difficulties of interpretation by someone else, particularly if the directions appear on the repair order.

A simple basis of assuming that you are facing the front of the property from the street, with rear, right and left consistently in their respective locations, works well, no matter how you view a particular element during your visit. It should also prove intelligible to repairers following after you. For example, in the rear garden, looking towards the rear wall of the house, the elements on the left are described as though you are facing from the front, i.e. on the right. By rigidly adopting such a basis for locations, the relationship between interior and exterior and between various internal features can be more readily assessed in the subsequent report.

The order in which rooms and areas are inspected also needs to be consistent. Start on the top floor, at the front right-hand room, moving to the front left-hand room, rear left-hand and rear right-hand room, i.e. in a clock-wise direction.

Within each room, first look at the ceiling, the floor, the front, left, rear and right-hand walls, including the window(s), the doors and the fittings, such as fires, sockets, airbricks, etc. within each of these elements.

Although this may seem an unnecessarily rigid method, it must be remembered that you will need to draft a report from your site notes, and that report may need to be interpreted and checked by others. If you jump from interior to exterior and introduce random elements into your notes, you will have to rearrange these and edit them before reporting or be faced at a later date with an embarrassing challenge to your methodology, or lack of it.

Using the senses

The use of a person's senses cannot be underestimated. Tools and equipment are merely there to assist you. Each inspection requires the application of all your senses. *Smell and taste* – for damp, mould, sewage, gas leak, etc. *Hearing* – for water leaks, central heating faults, bird infestations. *Sight* – for discolouration, blemishes, missing components. *Touch* – for dampness, looseness of materials, strength and operation of components.

Our senses will often give us more ready warning of a defect than the instruments, which are then used to analyse, investigate and assist in the diagnosis of what has already been identified as a possible problem.

Identifying defects

The inspection, and consequently the notes taken, needs to be informed by the diagnosis of the defect based on the information in chapter 3 and Appendix II as well as other sources. There will be occasions when the housing manager cannot be certain of the cause of the defect or, on occasions, the next stage of investigation required to get to the underlying cause. In such cases, the defect should be reported on the information of which the manager is certain, probably the visible symptoms, together with any indicators as to underlying cause(s) which he or she feels may apply.

Inspection notes

The notes taken at the inspection will form the basis of future action and your response to the complaints of the tenant. The notes need to be sufficiently comprehensive to give you a picture of the dwelling and to record its actual, past and potential relevant defects. They need to be written in such a way that you will be able to interpret them and use them as an *aide-mémoire* both on your immediate return to the office and at a later date, perhaps over a year later.

The notes should be written in ink, not pencil. They should be written legibly so that others can also read them. Abbreviations should be either commonly-used or self-explanatory. Idiosyncratic acronyms should be avoided. The notes will include some descriptive matter to set the scene in which the defects themselves are to be viewed. A sample table of notes of an inspection of a typical terraced house is set out below. Although these are typed, they are merely the notes taken on site. The report drawn from these notes is given later.

Numbering of rooms, areas and noted items is a good method of ordering the notes. It can assist to shorten note taking where particular features are repeated and allows for ready cross-referencing, for example from interior to exterior.

In the sample notes set out below a summary of the diagnosis is given alongside. This diagnosis is not written out in full but indicates the questions needed to be asked and the route of enquiry.

The inclusion of notes in parentheses [....] can be a useful tool if the draft is to be immediately converted into a report. The format of reports is dealt with in chapter 6, but throughout the process the end-result must be kept in view.

The notes taken at the time are the primary source of information from which future actions will flow. Accuracy of information collection is essential and time taken at this stage will pay rewards later.

Notes made during the inspection are contemporaneous notes and as such will form an integral part of evidence which may be presented in court at a later date. Giving evidence is covered in chapter 9, but it may be that reference to these notes will be the sole source of refreshing the memory in the witness box. See A. Kilpatrick *Repairs and Maintenance*, ch. 10 pp. 132-3.

SAMPLE TABLE OF NOTES AND DIAGNOSIS

Ref	Note	Diagnosis
1.	**First Floor**	
1.1	*Front room (Bedroom)*	
1.1.1	Mould growth to inside of steel [single-glazed] window frames	Steel windows are very vulnerable to condensation and single glazing means that more moisture will condense on and run down from the glass onto the frame and cill. Water condensing out on the frames will give rise to mould growth. Is there any other source of moisture?
1.1.2	Mould growth to ceiling to front wall junction	The location of the mould at the wall junction suggests condensation due to cold-bridging. Is there any other source of moisture? If so, the area would be expected to be damp.
1.1.3	Outlets from drain channels to middle rail of window filled	These channels should drain the water condensing on the inside of the windows.
1.1.4	Timber sub-frame to window rotten and opening at joints	The rot is caused by moisture which in the early stages will cause joints to swell and open up. The inside of the window is likely to get this moisture

SAMPLE TABLE OF NOTES AND DIAGNOSIS

Ref	Note	Diagnosis
1.1.4	[cont.]	from the condensation running down the inside of the window glass and frame, but is there any rot on the outside of the frame? Is the inside more rotten (soft) than the outside?
1.2	*Rear left-hand room (Bedroom)*	
1.2.1	Mould growth to inside of steel [single-glazed] window frames	Repeat of 1.1.1
1.2.2	Mould growth to ceiling to front wall junction [calor gas heater in front cupboard – no gas cylinder]	The gas heater, if used, will discharge considerable water vapour into the dwelling. The discharge will affect the whole dwelling not just the room in which it is used. Has it been in recent use?
1.2.3	Outlets from drain channels to middle rail of window filled	Repeat of 1.1.3
1.2.4	Timber sub-frame to window rotten and opening at joints	Repeat of 1.1.4
1.3	*Rear right-hand room (Bathroom/WC)*	
1.3.1	Glass to window cracked [possibly hit by stone from outside]	Cracks in glazing with an impact point may be due to damage not falling within the obligation to repair. Can the cause of the cracked glass be seen?
1.3.2	Mould growth to steel [single-glazed] window frame	Repeat of 1.1.1
1.3.3	Outlets from drain channels to middle rail of window filled	Repeat of 1.1.3

SAMPLE TABLE OF NOTES AND DIAGNOSIS

Ref	Note	Diagnosis
1.3.4	Timber sub-frame to window rotten and holed externally	Repeat of 1.1.4, but in this case there is damage externally suggesting a cause additional to condensation.
1.3.5	Mould growth to ceiling to right-hand 1.000 and extending along rear wall junction to left-hand corner [air grille rear wall high level papered over]	Repeat of 1.1.2. The blocking of the air grille will reduce the discharge of moisture-laden air from the room, increasing the likelihood of condensation. The opening of the grille will probably reduce the temperature in the room and will not be as effective as a powered extract fan.
1.3.6	WC pan loose on floor [no leaks]	Why is the pan loose? Is the floor rotten? Is the instability causing leakage which could cause rot or other damage, or even allow soil to discharge onto the floor?
1.3.7	Washbasin loose on left-hand wall and basin cracked [small indentation looks like impact damage, recent]	Is the crack clean and fresh? Does it have any indications of impact? These may affect whether it is the Landlord's liability to repair.
1.3.8	Door holed at base and centre adjoining lock stile [probable deliberate damage – trying to force open]	When was the damage caused and how? This may affect whether it is the Landlord's liability to repair.
2.	*Ground Floor*	
2.1	*Front left-hand room (Living Room)*	
2.1.1	Dampness (75 WME) to front wall and plaster perished and loose to average height 850, with section missing (approx 300 x 200) to left of window. [no injection holes out-	What is the moisture meter reading? Is there a sharp change in readings? Are there any visible signs of deterioration to decorations or plaster? Is the skirting board of timber and is it damp and/or rotten? All these help to assess the possible source and the seriousness of the defect. What is the wall type? Is there a visible damp-proof course? Is the plaster hard or soft? These

SAMPLE TABLE OF NOTES AND DIAGNOSIS

Ref	Note	Diagnosis
	side, solid brick wall, no visible dpc, sharp reduction in meter readings at top of damp area]	help to indicate possible areas of failure of the structure and the direction of any further investigations. The information obtained indicates a problem of dampness due to an ineffective barrier to rising damp.
2.1.2	Dampness (20 WME) to rear internal wall to height 100 [solid block wall, no visible plaster damage, no visible dpc, gradual reduction in meter readings at top of damp area, no mould but Tenant claims that the skirting gets mouldy]	Repeat of 2.1.1. In this case the information indicates condensation as the most likely cause, due to lower temperature of the wall where it is in close proximity to the ground.
2.1.3	Mould growth to inside of steel window frames [no mould to reveals or plasterwork and decorations adjoining]	Repeat of 1.1.1
2.1.2	No permanent ventilation to room – gas fire fitted to fireplace	The Gas Safety Regulations require Landlords to ensure that all gas appliances are safe for use. In general, all appliances other than some balanced flue units and small gas fires require permanent ventilation. Annual checks are mandatory.
2.1.3	Door binds on frame and hinges loose	How did the door become loose? Is there evidence of deliberate damage? Is the frame defective or have the screw holes become oversized and worn through old age?
2.1.4	Outlets from drain channels to middle rail of windows filled	Repeat of 1.1.3
2.1.5	Timber sub-frame to front window rotten and opening at joints	Repeat of 1.1.4

SAMPLE TABLE OF NOTES AND DIAGNOSIS

Ref	Note	Diagnosis
2.1.6	Timber sub-frame to left-hand window rotten and holed	Repeat of 1.1.4
2.2	*Rear left-hand room (Kitchen)*	
2.2.1	Peeling paintwork to ceiling and mould growth to rear left-hand corner	Repeat of 1.1.2. The non operation of the fan (see 2.2.3) will reduce the discharge of moisture-laden air from the room, increasing the likelihood of condensation.
2.2.2	Mould growth to pvc window frame [double-glazed]	Pvc windows with double glazing are not usually vulnerable to condensation. However, the non operation of the fan will reduce the discharge of moisture-laden air from the room, increasing the likelihood of condensation.
2.2.3	Electric extract fan not operating [electric outlet indicator light on]	Why has the fan failed? Has it been disconnected by the occupants? Is the electricity on – i.e. has any pre-payment meter been charged?
2.2.4	Loose floorboarding to front of centre adjoining doorway	This is a ground floor and the sub-floor timbers are always vulnerable to dampness either from the ground or from the dwelling. Ventilation of the void is essential. Are the boards loose because the supporting timbers are rotten? This may require further investigation which cannot be carried out at the initial visit.
2.2.5	Hinge stile of door broken away at mid-height	When was the damage caused and how? This may affect whether it is the Landlord's liability to repair. It may have been an attempted break-in.
2.2.6	Outlets from drain channels to cill of window filled	Repeat of 1.1.3
2.2.7	Waste trap to sink leaking in cupboard and shelving to cupboard saturated and disintegrating	If this is left unrepaired, further rapid deterioration of the cupboard will occur.

SAMPLE TABLE OF NOTES AND DIAGNOSIS

Ref	Note	Diagnosis
2.3	*Hall*	
2.3.1	Dampstaining to soil pipe duct within rear cupboard indicates leakage from pipework serving upper unit (no . . .)	Without access to the upper unit it is not possible to assess the cause. It may be a defect caused by misuse in the flat above. Further investigation is required.
3.	**Exterior**	
3.1	*Front elevation*	
3.1.1	No projecting drip to head of window sub-frames	This may relate to the window and ceiling/wall defects noted in each room. If there is no projecting drip, water will tend to run into the junction between the head of the window and the wall. This could cause dampness internally and by making the wall damp, increase the cold bridge effect, in turn increasing the likelihood of condensation.
3.2	*Left-hand flank elevation*	
3.2.1	Metal drip to head of window directs water onto timber sub-frame	This may relate to the window defects noted in each room. The direction of water onto the external cill may be the primary cause of the rot to the cill.
3.3	*Rear Elevation*	
3.3.1	Metal drip to head of windows directs water onto timber sub-frame	Repeat of 3.2.1.
3.3.2	Dampstaining to brickwork on line of soil pipe further indicates leakage (see 2.3.1 above)	This reinforces the indication that there is a long-standing leak from the pipe and that further investigation is required. See 2.3.1.

Example

An inspection of a sample property, resulting in the notes set out above, might proceed as follows:

The manager arrives, with or without colleagues, and introduces her/himself to the tenant. The manager explains the purpose of the inspection and that in order to put the matters in context, some appreciation of the area and adjoining buildings is required. The manager briefly looks around the immediate neighbourhood and at the relationship of the subject property to the adjoining buildings or sites, noting the addresses of those adjoining sites or buildings, or their location where no address exists.

Returning to the premises, the manager will knock again and explain that an inspection of the interior will be followed by the exterior and possibly some discussion with the tenant. The tenant should be invited to confirm the nature of the reported defect, but the manager should resist chasing after a series of randomly located defects rather than inspecting the dwelling on a methodical basis.

Armed with the originating information and any elaboration of this or additional matters raised by the tenant, the manager starts to inspect.

Following the recommended order of inspection (see above), the manager goes to the top front room first. The inspection of this room will follow the pattern for all interior spaces and the following description of this process, therefore, has a general application.

The first tools to be used are the eyes! Locate the room mentally in the dwelling, note whether there are any other rooms on the same floor and how they compare in overall size to the subject room. This mental preparation is probably the least tangible but an essential prerequisite to a successful inspection of the space. Look around the room, take in its general arrangement and how the elements fit together to check that the pre-conceived scheme will be suitable. For example, it may be necessary to add a further category to allow for a bulkhead or off-set wall, or windows on more than one elevation.

It may be helpful to sketch the layout. If so, a few simple rules need to be applied: Wherever possible use squared paper which makes sketching much easier. Sketch the external outline of the dwelling in plan with the front external wall at the top of the page, leaving a generous margin for any notes or features. Then infill with the rooms. Draw the rooms so that later the shape and features of the space can be recognised.

Mentally compile a list of the elements and start with the ceiling. Observe the layout, assess its possible construction and its condition. Look for "trigger defects" (see Appendix II) and record them, including their approximate location. Always look into built-in cupboards. Because they are often built to enclose awkward junctions between walls and ceilings or in corners of rooms, they can conceal serious defects not yet reported by the tenant but which will worsen if ignored.

The description should be brief but contain the salient points which can best be illustrated by the following example, which is not an exhaustive list of possible elements of construction, but does give an indication of the information which can be gleaned.

Ceiling	
Item	*Possible description*
Decoration	Painted on finish surface
	Painted on paper
	Papered
	Undecorated
Finish	Plasterboard
	Plaster (lath & plaster)
	Other boarding
Structure	Ceiling joists
(assessed not necessarily seen)	Floor joists
	Concrete roof
	Concrete floor

Follow the ceiling with the floor. Note how it is covered and whether it can be lifted. If so, check the structural covering to get an indication of the type of construction of the building.

Next observe the walls, including the elements such as windows and doors contained within them. Open windows and doors to check their operation and adequacy of fit. Lift doors gently by the handles to check for movement on hinges. Assess the effectiveness of external doors and windows to minimise draughts and water penetration. Use views from the windows to observe low-level roofs and pipes. Test the condition of the window cill and sub-cill. Although part of the exterior, these elements are convenient to include with the interior. Refer to the Checklist in App. II p. 163 for additional information to be gathered based on particular visible defects.

Proceed with the other elements to complete the

picture of the room. Before leaving the room, take a look around to refresh your overall impression. This is the opportunity to take photographs to act as *aides-mémoires* (see p. 76).

Continue to other areas/rooms in the house, following a methodical order, and repeat the process. This should not take long in rooms/areas where there are no defects. The descriptions can be brief and include acronyms and abbreviations. The whole process can be refined and streamlined with a relatively small amount of self-training and practice. To inspect one room will take significantly less time than it takes to read about the process in this book!

Proceed floor by floor to the lowest floor. Include, but identify as distinct from the demised premises, the common parts providing either cover, access to, or escape from the premises. Include areas to which access is necessary to check service meters or to turn off supplies in an emergency.

From the lowest floor interior, where the inspection should finish in the rear room, go to the rear exterior. Deal first with the rear wall(s) of the dwelling and the building within which it is contained. Log each wall of the elevations. Often there will be separate parts of the rear, usually containing the kitchen and bathroom. These need to be identified separately to ease cross-referencing to the interior and to ensure that all elements of the building are included. The side (flank) elevations are then dealt with, followed by the front. Again differentiate between the main walls and subsidiary structures such as bays, porches and any lean-to.

The inspection can then move to the side, the front and rear gardens and any access paths. The extent to which these are included in the landlord's obligation to repair is discussed in A. Kilpatrick *Repairs and Maintenance*, ch. 2 pp. 12-14. Notwithstanding the obligations on the parties, the description and condition of paths, fences, gates and access areas as well as out-houses, garages, etc. should be recorded.

Cross refer interior to exterior before leaving the premises to ensure that the trail has been followed as far as possible and that internal defects have been linked to external disrepair wherever possible.

There will always be defects which have no immediately obvious cause. These do not require resolution at the premises but may be matters which require either access equipment or specialist advice. Try to assemble as much information on these items as possible so that future action can be planned and discussions back in the office made as effective as possible.

Before finally departing, check through the notes, ensure that all areas have been inspected, or note those areas where no inspection has been carried out. Make sure that the notes are legibile.

Have a final discussion with the occupant giving, wherever possible, an indication of the time it will take to analyse the findings and decide on what action, if any, to take. Try not to promise works or other action unless these can be delivered with confidence and only give timescales that are certain to be achieved.

Timescales

To give dates or undertakings which may not be delivered may bind the landlord and give ammunition to any opponents should the matter proceed to litigation. There is a widely held belief among tenants, particularly in the public sector, that any timescales will be exceeded and that any undertakings will be broken. This is not always a justified view but, nevertheless, it is a common perception. Accordingly, although occupants may consider that the works which they perceive as required should be carried out immediately, they will be more concerned that what they are told will in fact happen. Without wishing to suggest evasive responses, it is probably better to offer a response in a few days after full consideration.

Timescales within which local authorities make repairs are required to be published (section 167 of the Local Government and Housing Act 1989). Even without these timescales, many social landlords set their own guidelines and targets. Although adherence to these is important, they can apply only if the repairs are not complex or the causes uncertain (see pp. 119-20, below).

Do-It-Yourself

Sometimes it is very tempting to carry out a minor repair oneself. For example, where an extract fan is not working, a simple test is to change the fuse. If this allows the fan to operate, then there is no point in removing the good fuse to replace the defective one, just to maintain the defect. However, there still remains the question of why the fuse blew. The defect is not fully repaired until the cause of the failure has been identified and/or the problem repaired with confidence of its future safe performance. Any such repairs must be noted so that there is a record of the action and others who will follow will know what has been tried. Avoid the temptation to get things going or carry out repairs which could fail. First, a housing manager is not a trained building operative and is exceeding her/his job description in carrying out repairs. Secondly, if the repair is one for which the landlord, is not liable, the execution of work by a housing manager may give rise to a claim that the additional liability has been accepted. Thirdly, should the repair fail, the landlord and the manager could be liable for that failure and any consequential losses.

PART III

POST-INSPECTION
PRACTICE

CHAPTER 6

REPORTING

**Customers / The findings /
Format /** *Core section /
Supplementary sections /
Record note / Landlord's liability /
Tenant's liability /
Reference to further action*

The reporting process, like the note taking on site, is an essential ingredient to deal effectively with disrepair and to minimise the risk of recurrence of defects or further complaints.

It is not the function of this book to set out "master procedures" for housing managers. To do so would deny all the experiences of individuals and the diverse but often equally effective processes already in place. However, the benefits of following controllable and comprehensive procedures can really be illustrated only with examples. This chapter therefore deals with aims and objectives of reporting using examples rather than setting these out as the only methods which are acceptable.

Customers

Reporting is a means of communicating what was seen on site and informing the future actions or considerations of others and of the author. Therefore before starting to write the report, the manager will need to establish who are his or her readers or customers. Using the concept of customers is a TQM (Total Quality Management) technique. A simple question and answer help to explain and define this concept, Q: Who are your customers? A: Anyone who receives a product or service from you.

These customers will be both internal and external. The internal customers are the manager's colleagues who have to take action based on his or her information. This may, of course, include the manager's future actions and responses and those of other allied departments of the organisation such as Legal, Building Works, Technical Services, etc. These are discussed in succeeding chapters. External customers will probably be limited to the end-user (the tenant), but may also include insurers and management committees who will have demands of their own which need to be satisfied by the process adopted.

The findings

By rechecking the initial note of complaint, it will be possible to modify the perception of what was initially thought to be clear in the light of the information obtained from the visit. For example, the initial report may have referred to a specific defect which on inspection was found to be one of a number of equal or greater concern. The tenants may have indicated the involvement of their own advisers and possibly an expert, or suggested that litigation was being contemplated where no previous indication was given.

The findings of the inspection may also send signals that litigation is a possibility. There may be defects which, although serious, the housing manager knows do not fit into the landlord's current scheme for repairs and will therefore take a revision of policy to resolve. Such matters as condensation-caused dampness can easily give rise to litigation long before any changes in policy, let alone availability of funds for works.

It may not be only the possibility of litigation which sets the format and content of the report. The defects found may be ones which the housing manager knows will be addressed in a future rehabilitation scheme or a larger package of improvements. Such major schemes will often preclude expenditure on interim repairs which will be undone by the major scheme. Nevertheless, there may be a genuine need to address the repair of defects in the short term. This is especially the case with estate-wide improvement schemes which depend on the vagaries of the public sector housing finance system. This can often make the timing of such schemes seem more a matter of chance, rather like a lottery, than planned (see also chapter 7).

In such cases it may be that the housing manager has to argue within the landlord's organisation for expenditure in advance of the major scheme.

Format

In order to respond to the variety of customers and consequences of findings, the format of the report must be as flexible as possible. To achieve this, reports are best produced as a series of components which can be arranged and re-arranged to suit the changing needs of the customers.

The core section of the report will be the conditions found on site. This will, however, need to be divided into those matters which require action, and those which are for the record and may need to be drawn on at a later date. There might also need to be an overview of the conditions found and preliminary views on the liability of the parties, as well as recommendations for future action and time priorities.

The use of standard formats for each of these components will enable a higher level of quality control and will maximise use of the scarcest resource, the housing manager's time. The following component formats are suggestions only. Their inclusion here is to illustrate their content rather than to set out rigid rules which have to be applied.

Core section

The report's core section summarises the information gathered on defects and identifies the repairs that are required. There will be occasions when the housing manager is not certain either of the cause of the defect or of the remedial works required. In such cases, the defect should be reported on the basis of the information about which the manager is certain, probably the visible symptoms, together with any indicators as to underlying cause in which he or she feels confidence. The repairs required may be limited at this stage to further investigation, possibly by an expert (see ch. 9 pp. 138-139).

Using the example of the notes set out in chapter 5, and the descriptions in chapter 3 and Appendix II, it is possible to provide a schedule of defects and a brief outline of the repairs which may be required. A sample schedule is set out below. Some of these items, for example 2.1.1, will require an expert to diagnose the cause of the defect and specify the repair.

SCHEDULE OF DEFECTS AND REPAIRS

Note: all directions taken facing the front of the premises from the street

Ref	Defect	Repair
1.	*First Floor*	
1.1	*Front room (Bedroom)*	
1.1.1	Mould growth to inside of steel window frames	Following repairs to window sub-frames, remove mould and make good to decorations.
1.1.2	Mould growth to ceiling to front wall junction	Remove mould and make good to decorations.
1.1.3	Outlets from drain channels to middle rail of window filled	Clean out drain outlets and make good to decorations.
1.1.4	Timber sub-frame to window rotten and opening at joints	Renew sub-frame complete and make good to plaster and decorations disturbed.
1.2	*Rear left-hand room (Bedroom)*	

SCHEDULE OF DEFECTS AND REPAIRS

Note: all directions taken facing the front of the premises from the street

Ref	Defect	Repair
1.2.1	Mould growth to inside of steel window frames	Following repairs to window sub-frames, remove mould and make good to decorations.
1.2.2	Mould growth to ceiling to front wall junction	Remove mould and make good to decorations.
1.2.3	Outlets from drain channels to middle rail of window filled	Clean out drain outlets and make good to decorations.
1.2.4	Timber sub-frame to window rotten and opening at joints	Renew sub-frame complete and make good to plaster and decorations disturbed.
1.3	*Rear right-hand room (Bathroom/WC)*	
1.3.1	Glass to window cracked	Renew glazing, make good to putties and decorations.
1.3.2	Mould growth to steel window frame	Following repairs to window sub-frames, remove mould and make good to decorations.
1.3.3	Outlets from drain channels to middle rail of window filled	Clean out drain outlets and make good to decorations.
1.3.4	Timber sub-frame to window rotten and holed externally	Renew sub-frame complete and make good to plaster and decorations disturbed.
1.3.5	Mould growth to ceiling to right-hand 1.000 and extending along rear wall junction to left-hand corner	Remove mould and make good to decorations.

SCHEDULE OF DEFECTS AND REPAIRS

Note: all directions taken facing the front of the premises from the street

Ref	Defect	Repair
1.3.6	WC pan loose on floor	Securely fix pan to floor.
1.3.7	Washbasin loose on left-hand wall and basin cracked	Renew basin and securely fix to wall; run mastic seal to wall tiling junction.
1.3.8	Door holed at base and centre adjoining lock stile	Reface door and make good to decorations.
2.	*Ground Floor*	
2.1	*Front left-hand room (Living Room)*	
2.1.1	Dampness (75 WME) to rear wall and plaster perished and loose to average height 850, with section missing (approx 300 x 200) to left of window	Remove skirting board and check condition/ existence of damp-proof course. Assess and execute necessary remedial work including renewal of plaster, skirtings, etc.
2.1.2	Dampness (20 WME) to front wall to height 100	Remove skirting board and verify that dampness is limited to condensation.
2.1.3	Mould growth to inside of steel window frames	Following repairs to window sub-frames, remove mould and make good to decorations.
2.1.4	No permanent ventilation to room – gas fire fitted to fireplace	Carry out checks in accordance with Gas Safety Regulations and install permanent ventilation if required. Make good to plaster and decorations disturbed.
2.1.5	Door binds on frame and hinges loose	Adjust and rehang door; make good to decorations.
2.1.6	Outlets from drain channels to middle rail of windows filled	Clean out drain outlets and make good to decorations.

SCHEDULE OF DEFECTS AND REPAIRS

Note: all directions taken facing the front of the premises from the street

Ref	Defect	Repair
2.1.7	Timber sub-frame to front window rotten and opening at joints	Renew sub-frame complete and make good to plaster and decorations disturbed.
2.1.8	Timber sub-frame to left-hand window rotten and holed	Renew sub-frame complete and make good to plaster and decorations disturbed.
2.2	*Rear left-hand room (Kitchen)*	
2.2.1	Peeling paintwork to ceiling and mould growth to rear left-hand corner	Remove mould and make good to decorations.
2.2.2	Mould growth to pvc window frame	Remove mould and make good to decorations.
2.2.3	Electric extract fan not operating	Test, overhaul and repair fan and leave in full working order.
2.2.4	Loose floorboarding to front of centre adjoining doorway	Lift boarding and inspect; repair as necessary so it's securely fixed down; make good to floor finish.
2.2.5	Hinge stile of door broken away at mid-height	Replace door and make good to decorations.
2.2.6	Outlets from drain channels to cill of window filled	Clean out drain outlets and make good to decorations.
2.2.7	Waste trap to sink leaking in cupboard and shelving to cupboard saturated and disintegrating	Remake joints to waste outlet, renew shelving complete and make good to any decorations disturbed.

SCHEDULE OF DEFECTS AND REPAIRS

Note: all directions taken facing the front of the premises from the street

Ref	Defect	Repair
2.3	*Hall*	
2.3.1	Dampstaining to soil pipe duct within Rear Cupboard indicates leakage from pipework serving upper unit (no . . .)	Inspect upper unit. Check and test pipework and repair as necessary; make good to boxing and decorations.
3.	*Exterior*	
3.1	*Front elevation*	
3.1.1	No projecting drip to head of window sub-frames	Following renewal of frames, fit projecting drip.
3.2	*Left-hand flank elevation*	
3.2.1	Metal drip to head of window directs water onto timber sub-frame	Following renewal of frames, fit projecting drip.
3.3	*Rear elevation*	
3.3.1	Metal drip to head of windows directs water onto timber sub-frame	Following renewal of frames, fit projecting drips.
3.3.2	Dampstaining to brickwork on line of soil pipe further indicates leakage (see 2.3.1 above)	See 2.3.1 above.

Supplementary sections

These can vary considerably and will require tailoring to the circumstances of each case. It will be possible to establish a menu from which the housing manager can choose the appropriate formula to supplement the core section, dealing with particular aspects such as alleged tenant misuse, previous incomplete or unsuccessful repairs, and earlier incorrect diagnoses.

Record note

This is required for file information and to put both the site notes (chapter 5) and the report in context for other staff. It will include a general description of the premises and notes on the overall conditions found. It should include reference to the photographs taken and any sketches made which will serve to illustrate either the general setting of the property or particular defects.

A record note should be produced in a typed form rather than handwritten. It should be brief and seek to answer a series of questions as set out in the table below. It does not need to be a questionnaire but can be produced in normal prose. Like a jigsaw, the relevance of each piece of information is fully appreciated only when the whole is completed. Although each aspect may appear simple and not contentious, it will be seen from chapters 7 and 9 that all these aspects have relevance.

SAMPLE RECORD NOTE	
Question	*Example*
Address	16 View Road, VW7 8AS
Who inspected	P. Reddin
Date of inspection	23 June 1995
Approximate time of inspection	15.30
Weather conditions	Heavy rain
Type of dwelling	Ground floor flat, 2 beds, living room, k&b
Type of block	4-storey purpose-built
Location	mid-terrace
Approximate date of construction	c.1890
Approximate date of substantial modernisation works	c.1975
Anticipated life	30 years
Number of occupants and approx. ages	Adults 1M, 2F Children 2-10 1M Children 0-2 1F
Heating	Gas fire LR
Ventilation	Airbricks to kitchen & bathroom

Landlord's liability

In order to assess the future action which needs to be taken, the liability of the landlord must be addressed. The primary source of the liabilities of the landlord will be the tenancy agreement. This ought to be read prior to the inspection but will need to be referred to again in the light of the defects found. Reference will also need to be made to the statutory provisions and common law, described in detail in A. Kilpatrick *Repairs and Maintenance,* chs. 2, 3 and 6.

The obligations of the landlord need to be related to the defects set out in the core section. Not all the defects will fall within the obligation to repair and these must be identified. It may be that some items of disrepair will still be rectified by the landlord as a matter of policy, but such works must be undertaken with authority as to do so may set a precedent committing the landlord to future liability.

An indication of the urgency of the repair should also be included. This is discussed in chapter 7 in relation to statutory provisions under the Tenants' Right to Repair and also guidance and good practice.

Tenant's liability

The tenancy agreement will usually set out the obligations of the tenant. In public sector social housing, this is usually restricted to the obligations not to commit waste, to use and keep the premises in tenantable repair and not to commit nuisance. See further A. Kilpatrick *Repairs and Maintenance*, ch. 7 pp. 106-109. There may be other obligations, including a prohibition on criminal use, on interference with quiet enjoyment of neighbours, etc. These are matters which a housing manager may wish to include in a report, but they are beyond the scope of this book.

Reference to further action

The housing manager will be able to draw preliminary conclusions from the information obtained on site. Based on this information, the future action required can be assessed and a plan of action implemented. The conclusion will need to include at least an initial list of other departments or persons who should be aware of the inspection and report. It does not necessarily mean that they need to see the report at this stage.

CHAPTER 7

PRIORITIES

External advice / Specification for repairs / Assessing priorities / *General factors / Statutory obligations / Codes of practice / Tenants' Guarantee / Tenants' Right to Repair / Chartered Institute of Housing Standards / Planned maintenance / Wholesale redevelopment or rehabilitation / Value for money*

The urgency for future action will have been determined initially by the housing manager as part of the report (see chapter 6). The action required could be the execution of repairs or it could be further investigation or guidance. As seen in chapter 5, there will be many occasions where accurate diagnosis of the cause of a defect and consequently the specification of the repair required will be beyond the competence of the housing manager, or not possible at the time of initial inspection. Housing managers are not engineers, surveyors or architects and are unlikely to possess sufficient technical skills to diagnose all defects fully. An inaccurate diagnosis could increase the liability of the landlord and confuse issues. It is essential that housing managers take a realistic and modest view of their technical skills and that there is available to them sufficient technical back-up where this is required.

External advice

The particular skills required to diagnose the defect may be available within the housing manager's organisation but, if not, external assistance and advice may have to be sought. In deciding the agency and person to whom a referral will be made consideration must be given to the following factors:

If the further investigation is purely of a technical nature, then referral should be on the basis of the person's or agency's track record of dealing with such matters. Often the organisation will maintain a list of consultants to whom particular categories of problem can be referred.

Where the further investigation will also require an expert opinion, which could be open to challenge in any subsequent court hearing, the selection is more critical. The referral will not be to an agency but to a specific individual. The appropriate selection criteria are described in chapter 9.

Specification for repairs

Only after carrying out the further investigations and receiving the advice sought, either from internal colleagues or from external sources, can the final list of repairs be drawn up. There is no set format for this and it will depend on the structure of the organisation how the works are implemented. The repair will, however,

now be sufficiently well specified to allow them to be
ordered. The orders should be unambiguous and readily understandable. Target times for completion need
also to be specified by the housing manager.

Assessing priorities

The priority for the repairs will need to be assessed
both on an individual and on a strategic basis. There
ought to be a stated relationship between planned and
reactive maintenance and an awareness of possible
forthcoming major schemes of renovation. Dissemi-
nation of strategic decisions and possible schemes
within the landlord's organisation is required. The existence of plans for major refurbishment should be known
to all housing managers, together with the current status and anticipated timescale.

General factors

Having assessed the liability for repair (see chapter
6 and A. Kilpatrick *Repairs and Maintenance*), the priority for the particular repair should be established.
Priority will be determined by the following factors
(discussed below):
- the statutory obligations of the landlord;
- the guidance available in codes of good practice;
- the planned works of repair already set in motion;
- the anticipated time before major works of renovation are executed or the property redeveloped;
- value for money.

Traditionally, the availability of resources will also
influence the priorities. The courts have nevertheless

generally not accepted the plea of "poverty" to excuse a landlord from obligations to repair (see A. Kilpatrick *Repairs and Maintenance*, ch. 5 p. 68). In the case of major works, however, which could have far-reaching effects on finance, the courts have been reluctant to include these in the landlord's repairing obligation.

As an example, the problem of condensation-caused dampness in local authority housing is one which seriously affects not just the enjoyment of those dwellings but also the health of the occupants. In civil actions, the courts have generally not accepted that the works required to remedy this defect (a combination of heating, insulation and ventilation) are within the landlord's repairing obligations as contained in section 11 of the Landlord and Tenant Act 1985, notwithstanding the actual and potential damaging effects on the occupants and the structure of the landlord's property (see further A. Kilpatrick *Repairs and Maintenance*, ch. 2 pp. 28-30 and ch. 4). Nevertheless, by using the Environmental Protection Act 1990, tenants have been able to secure orders from the magistrates court requiring works to remedy condensation dampness and mould growth. See A. Kilpatrick *Repairs and Maintenance*, ch. 6 p. 97.

The inclusion of an improvement within a repairing obligation will be allowed only where the marginal cost is minimal (see A. Kilpatrick *Repairs and Maintenance*, ch. 2 pp. 24-28). In this way the availability of finance can have an influence on the liability of the landlord to execute a particular repair.

The purpose of establishing priorities is to maximise the limited resources of the landlord to deal most effectively and equitably with the often conflicting demands of the occupants of the dwellings. In most cases, occupants would like all the repairs executed immediately, but equally they will accept that this may not be possible.

The factors described above require analysis in greater detail to understand their influence and relative importance in the establishment of the priority. To a large extent, priorities will be set by the organisation at a strategic level. The housing manager, however, needs to be aware of the criteria for these priorities as well as their use to determine the extent of work and response time in a particular case. These factors are now considered in turn.

Statutory obligations

Section 11(3) of the Landlord and Tenant Act 1985 limits the repairing obligation of the landlord by taking into account the age, character, location and prospective life of the dwelling. (See further A. Kilpatrick *Repairs and Maintenance*, ch. 2 pp. 14-16.) To give two extreme examples: the court will not order renewal of a roof covering where the whole building is to be redeveloped within a year; conversely, it will have little hesitation in ordering the renewal of a roof on a building in a neighbourhood of high quality dwellings with a prospective life of over 60 years. Unfortunately extreme examples are rare. It is the vast grey area in the middle which requires examination to establish some principles.

Codes of practice

In England and Wales local authorities are required by statute (section 167(1) of the Local Government and

Housing Act 1989) to assess and publish performance indicators. Similar provisions apply in Scotland under section 17A of the Housing (Scotland) Act 1987 and section 153 of the Leasehold Reform, Housing and Urban Development Act 1993. The detailed content required of these performance indicators varies within the UK, each set of requirements being drawn up by the relevant government department (Department of the Environment, Welsh Office, and Scottish Office). There is a common thread, however, which requires that each authority reports the priority levels, the target response times for each, and the achievements of that authority in meeting those targets.

Housing associations are not included in these statutory provisions, but in all three parts of the UK they are expected to publish similar information under the Tenants' Guarantee or the requirements of Scottish Homes (the regulator for housing associations in Scotland).

Tenants' Guarantee

The Tenants' Guarantee applies to housing associations in England and Wales (see C. Hunter *Tenants' Rights*, pp. 5-6 Arden's Housing Library vol. 2). Although slightly different in each part of the UK, the general thrust is the same. Housing associations are required to meet their statutory and contractual obligations to keep their housing fit for human habitation and to ensure it is well maintained. They are required to inspect the properties regularly and plan for future maintenance. Published priorities from both the local authorities and housing associations give indicators of priority categories and performance targets.

Tenants' Right to Repair
Reference should also be made to the law and guidance on the Tenants' Right to Repair. This legislation is intended to allow tenants to claim compensation for the landlord's failure to execute repairs satisfactorily within a given target period. The periods are set out in the Secure Tenants of Local Authorities (Right to Repair) Regulations 1994, SI 1994 No. 133 as amended by SI 1994 No. 844, for England and Wales and the Secure Tenants (Right to Repair) (Scotland) Regulations 1994, SI 1994 No. 1046. These provisions came into effect on 1 April 1994 in England and Wales and 1 October 1994 in Scotland. (See further A. Kilpatrick *Repairs and Maintenance*, ch. 5 pp. 85-88.)

Although the compensation rates are different and some classes of work do not appear in both Regulations, there is a general similarity. The Regulations set out periods of working days within which the authority is required to complete the repair. If this is not achieved, the tenant can require the landlord to send a second contractor and the period allowed is repeated. Failure to complete the repair by the expiry of this second period gives a right to compensation payable to the tenant by the landlord.

Both the Housing Corporation (in England) and Scottish Homes have introduced similar voluntary schemes. As yet, there is no scheme for Wales.

The result is that for the tenants of these authorities and associations, there is a published target for repair of specific defects. The accumulated period between report of a defect and the right to compensation is a useful indicator of the priority attached to any given repair and the overall target period that ought to be achieved.

Chartered Institute of Housing Standards

The Chartered Institute of Housing launched its *Housing Management Standards Manual* in 1994 and also established a Good Practice Unit. Together they provide useful benchmarks. The manual is updated regularly and describes the process of identifying varying priorities in response to disrepair and the suggested timescales for examples of defects. For instance, the table opposite is based on the examples of good practice in the *Housing Management Standards Manual*.

Planned maintenance

Planned maintenance falls into two categories: cyclical and programmed maintenance. Cyclical work is carried out at regular intervals to minimise the risk of premature deterioration, e.g. external painting. Programmed maintenance is work required to replace components, e.g. boilers, roof coverings, windows. Usually it is work carried out to a group of buildings as part of a modernisation scheme.

The priority for a repair cannot be assessed in isolation as though a particular dwelling which requires attention is the sole property within the landlord's portfolio. A balance must be struck between the overall repairing obligation of the landlord and the individual demands of a particular tenant.

Responsible landlords will have a plan which will allow for cyclical and programmed maintenance works to be carried out to their stock. The basic works will comprise external decorations and minor consequential repairs such as repointing, renewal of glazing putties and mastic, cleaning and repair of gutters and repairs to external doors and windows. They will also

Table of Repair Completion Targets for a Reasonable Landlord

Ref	Type	Example	Time from date of Report (weeks) Inspect	Order	Complete
A	Urgent Repairs	Defective ball valve Leaking radiator			1
B1	Normal or Routine Repairs Not Requiring Inspection	Leaking guttering; Windows that cannot be opened safely			4
B2	Normal or Routine Repairs Requiring Inspection	Dampness to plasterwork Fungal decay to timbers	2	3	7
C1	Planned Repairs Not Requiring Inspection	Rewiring; Damaged fencing Broken bath panel			10
C2	Planned Repairs Requiring Inspection	Defective floorboards Overhaul windows	6	8	18
E	Emergency Repair (i.e. Serious damage to the building; Danger to health; Risk to safety; Risk of loss or damage to occupier's property)	Falling masonry Flooding Complete failure of electrics	Immediate	Immediate	1 day

include renewal of components with a known life expectancy. The majority of such components will be parts of the service installations together with kitchen units. In some cases, planned maintenance also includes works which could be classed as improvements but which involve such small cost that they do not need to form part of a major scheme of renovation. Take, for example, extractor fans or powered ventilation systems to combat and minimise the effects of condensation.

Wholesale redevelopment or rehabilitation

The absence of new housing, the lack of availability of building land, the restriction on resources and the unexpectedly high costs of maintenance of some of the public sector housing stock built between 1955 and 1975 has resulted in political pressure for wholesale modernisation schemes. The response has been Estate Action Programmes, City Challenge or other one-off funding opportunities. In the context of repair timescales, these schemes add another generally imprecise variable.

It is reasonable to say that a landlord should not be obliged to carry out expensive and substantial works of repair when within a relatively short period all that work will be undone by a major renovation scheme. (See further A. Kilpatrick *Repairs and Maintenance*, ch. 2 pp. 14-16.) The difficulty arises primarily in the funding system, and this is perhaps best illustrated by an example.

Example

A local housing authority owns a large 1960s housing estate, including some high-rise blocks, built of non-traditional construction. The major problems on the estate are manifested in social unrest and high unemployment. The infrastructure suffers from vandalism the fabric of the dwellings is degraded, and most suffer from dampness. The external structure of the high-rise blocks is failing, allowing water penetration, and services such as lifts are at the end of their useful life.

The landlord authority recognises that responsive repairs are running at a very high level and costs are unusually high, yet serious defects still remain. It also recognises that the works really required will be major and of high capital cost. Access to funding for such works is primarily from central government, although this may be a "leverage exercise" to obtain additional funding from the private sector.

Government funding schemes rarely seem to work on a predictable or planned basis for the recipients. City Challenge, for example, is in effect a lottery, where competing bids from local authorities are assessed and only a few lucky winners get money. Those that do win get money for five years and are clearly in a much better position to plan and carry out major estate improvement programmes.

Other sources of government funding still seem more problematic. Those seeking funds are often perceived as exaggerating the costs and/or need, and those controlling the funds see their role as one of reducing the demand to a level which the supply can accommodate. The capital allocation from the government to local authorities through the Housing Investment Programme simply allows the authority to borrow up to the limit of the sum approved. Decisions about how much the authority can borrow are based less and less on the immediate needs for repair and improvement, and more on other performance indicators such as how well the authority fulfils its enabling role, the quality of its overall strategy and its housing management performance. Thus authorities with very pressing need to deal with estates like the one described above can easily get less money than those with far fewer problems.

A major improvement programme for an estate will usually take several years to complete. But the authority will know what capital allocation it will receive only one year at a time, and this allocation is not "ring fenced" to a particular scheme. A major improvement scheme can be planned over three years. In year one, enough allocation will be received to cover the plan for that year. In year two, a smaller overall allocation may be received because of the decision-making process outlined above. Meanwhile another estate could suddenly become a higher priority, perhaps where a fire has revealed some potentially fatal design defect that has to be remedied immediately. The combination of these factors is likely to mean that the authority has to push much of its programme for the original estate from year two to year three.

The overall effect of this is that a local authority, for example, could rightly say that a dwelling should be included in a major renovation scheme within the next two or three years, thus lowering the standard of repair immediately required and affecting the priority of some repair works. The occupants may reasonably be expected to endure conditions which will be overcome in a couple of years; but what if funding does not arrive and the works are not put in hand after, say, three years? The landlord may still assert that the renovation scheme will occur within two or three years. Even if this does happen, this would mean that the occupants have endured the conditions not for two years as originally anticipated, but for five or six years. The period could of course be longer, and unpredictable. The anticipated life of the dwelling, which was at the beginning two years or so, may well in reality be 10 years.

Value for money

Where, for example, windows are made of timber and some, but not all, are rotten and require repair, the most cost-effective repair would be renewal. If the dwelling is one of a number with similar defects, the obvious way to maximise value for money is to place an order for a complete window replacement. What is the landlord to do? The tenant should not be expected to endure rotten windows for an unknown period. The dwelling demands a standard of repair which will include sound and well-repaired windows. Yet the landlord must balance these considerations against the value-for-money criterion. If a firm date for a window renewal programme is available, the courts are likely to be sympathetic to the landlord deferring repair. However, in the absence of precise dates for such works it is likely that a repair of the windows could be ordered as a result of legal action.

Another value-for-money consideration will have the effect of bringing forward a repair which may otherwise be deferred. Where access equipment, such as scaffolding, is required to carry out some repair works sooner than the particular repair being considered, but that same access equipment will be required to execute the particular repair, then it makes economic sense for the landlord to execute both repairs together.

An example would be the repointing of a chimney stack. Defective pointing is a defect which degrades relatively slowly. It would normally be left until a convenient time when access is readily available. If, however, a chimney pot has fallen off, possibly blown off in a storm, and requires urgent repair, similar access will be required. The extra cost of executing the repointing as part of the reinstatement of the chimney pot will probably be marginal, and it would make sense to execute both together.

The desirability of executing a repair earlier is not likely to persuade a court to order a shorter period for that repair, whereas deferring a repair for a period in the interests of value for money has been accepted as reasonable. The length of deferment is one of consideration on merits and expert opinion (see chapter 9).

CHAPTER 8

FOLLOW-UP ACTION

Monitoring performance /
Management systems / **Tenants'
satisfaction surveys / Redecoration /
Variations of the works /
Longer-term action /**
*Monitoring short-term repairs /
Visits and revisits*

It is central to the effective management of the properties that essential repairs are executed at the appropriate time. In most cases where absence of prompt
implementation of works has occurred it is due to a
combination of factors. The housing manager may lack
time, expertise or assertiveness and may be satisfied
that once the works are ordered, the responsibility
ceases. Those responsible for carrying out the works
may set priorities not by the need for the works to be
executed but by the availability of skilled workers and
materials. The use of external contractors can pose the
same problems and, in many cases, increase the diversity
of conflicting priorities.

Monitoring performance

Many local authorities are assessing and publishing details on the relative performance of different contractors. As was seen in chapter 7, performance measurement is now a statutory or regulatory requirement and the assessment of individual contractors' performance is an integral part of this. These requirements also oblige local authorities and housing associations to have much better systems for tracking repairs, and in particular to be able to pinpoint areas where they are under-achieving, by geographic location, contractor and priority band.

Nonetheless, the basic ingredient which remains essential is effective monitoring of the whole process by the housing manager.

Management systems

The housing manager requires tools to assist in performance assessment. Although the tools could be manual, to maximise effectiveness electronic systems should be used. These can comprise an electronic system of records linked to a database and diary which automatically notifies the housing manager of the approach of a deadline for completion, of the anticipated date of execution and generates chasing correspondence to ensure that times are achieved.

It is not the function of this book to describe, analyse or to design such systems but the principal demands which the housing manager should make of such a system can be considered. The key pieces of information required are:

- When was the order placed?

- When is it to be completed?
- To achieve completion, when will it need to start?
- When was it started?
- When was it completed?
- If delayed, why are works delayed, and what are the revised dates for start and completion of works?

By monitoring the execution of the works, the housing manager is able to ensure that target times are kept.

Tenants' satisfaction surveys

Increasingly, social housing landlords are asking their tenants to complete satisfaction forms. These are useful tools not just to produce statistics of customer satisfaction, but to indicate both successes and deficiencies in the repairs service. However, tenants do not always complete the forms and logging responses absorbs resources which often cannot be spared.

Those that respond confirming all works are satisfactory and completion within the target time can be analysed as part of the statistical audit. The returned forms which by their date suggest that works were completed late should generate a cross-check to the data collated above. The forms which express dissatisfaction either with the works or with the time taken should again be cross-checked.

With major works, there will be a supervisor and a contract administrator responsible to their landlord client for confirming that works are satisfactorily completed and that payment can be made. A record of this note of satisfaction should be available to the housing manager.

Perhaps the most important source of information

on the adequacy of repairs is any subsequent further complaint by the tenant. Complaint records vary widely, but some systems are designed to confuse and conceal relevant information. For example, one local authority's computerised records system was designed so that complaints were over-written with each modification. The effect of this was that after the repairs were completed, there was no readily accessible record to show that the defect originally complained of had in fact been rectified.

However, computerised databases are considerably more sophisticated and integrated repairs and ordering systems are in place in many local authority and housing association offices. Everything relating to a particular property can be accessed through the database and, conversely, no information about the property can be recorded without it appearing in the system. Each piece of information is identifiable so that the date and source of each entry can be traced. Overwriting can be prevented and records are made cumulatively. The advances in such programme design are rapid and already systems can generate a daily report to housing managers showing, for example, which repairs are outstanding beyond the target date.

Redecoration

Additional to the repairs will be the question of consequential works. In housing disrepair such consequential works will primarily involve redecoration, which traditionally has been seen as a tenant's responsibility. If redecoration has been necessary following execution of works by the landlord, then this has commonly either been left for the tenant to do, or a minimal contribution has been made towards materials on the basis that the tenant was intending to redecorate in any event.

Neither of these solutions is attractive for the tenant. With no contribution, the landlord may have repaired the defect but has not restored decorations to their condition before the defect occurred – or that is the perception of the tenant. The landlord conversely will take the view that if the decorations were poor prior to the defect, then no consequential loss has occurred. Assistance on the law on this aspect can be found in the case of *McGreal v Wake* (1984) 13 HLR 107 (see A. Kilpatrick *Repairs and Maintenance*, ch. 5 p. 77).

Variations of the works

Changes may occur in the works required in two ways. First, the works may have had to be specified as provisional until exposure of concealed areas allowed exact detailing of the repair. Secondly, there may be further works or consequential works arising out of the repairs.

When specifying works, it is often necessary to allow for two or more options, the selection of which will be made either solely by the operative or by a supervisor. An example of a defect which will require a series of repair works to remedy it is low level dampness to the walls of the lowest floor of a dwelling. The defect which can be identified on inspection is the dampness to the wall. Assuming that only limited testing has been carried out (see chapter 3), the order for works will need to allow for some exposure of the wall, to be followed by a decision on remedial work. This allowance for options or variations must be built into any ordering process and into the records of the housing manager. This type of defect may also require the execution of one or more repairs, followed by a period of monitoring, before further works are specified.

The works actually undertaken need to be recorded so that (i) they can be checked against the options envisaged, (ii) they can be referred to later should the initial works not prove wholly successful, and (iii) the experience can assist in building up a source of knowledge both in relation to the particular dwelling and in relation to the type of defect found.

Because some works will not be fully identifiable at inspection stage, further major works may become apparent during the course of relatively simple repairs. For example, the problem of a loose floorboard on the ground floor of a dwelling may without intervention and inspection at an early stage conceal a substantial outbreak of fungal decay. Having started the works, there is little option but to continue. However, the cost and scale of the works may change significantly and cause substantial unanticipated disruption to the occupants. The eradication of fungal decay may require the use of toxic materials which will mean that the occupants have to be temporarily housed elsewhere.

The procedures in place for the implementation of repairs and their monitoring by the housing manager must include a mechanism for such unexpected emergency situations. Equally, such situations will underline the need to carry out as much investigation and pre-planning of the works as possible.

Longer-term action

Initial repair works, may point up deficiencies which need to be addressed, both in terms of the long-term maintenance of the property value and in terms of healthy and acceptable standards for occupation by a tenant.

Many authorities and associations are, for example, now using the National Home Energy Rating Scheme, particularly through stock condition surveys. This gives a thermal insulation value for each dwelling from 0 (non-existent) to 10 (excellent). Targets are then set, for example to achieve a rating of 5 for all homes within three years, and 7 within six years. Allied to this are targets for reduction in the number and cost of repairs. One of the most common of such defects is condensation-caused dampness. To eradicate this defect fully, a combination of insulation, ventilation and affordable heating is required. However, the work done by the landlord may be limited to one of these three elements, probably the installation of extractor fans in the kitchen and bathroom, which is the cheapest option. It may be that further works, such as the installation of fixed electric heaters, are also carried out but that these are of minimal effect unless the running costs are affordable by the occupants. As explained in chapter 3, the presence of dampness causes many problems and should be remedied, even though to do so with full effect may exceed the repairing obligation. A procedure should be in place for the identification of major works or improvements to overcome the need for repeated repairs and to safeguard the landlord's property.

Monitoring short-term repairs

Defects require monitoring where short-term works have been executed with the expectation that longer-term solutions will be implemented in a known timescale, and when those solutions then cannot be or are not implemented.

The short-term solution can sometimes outlive its anticipated life. Where repairs of a known limited life expectancy have been executed because of the forthcoming scheme of works, it is only equitable that the defect should be revisited when the circumstances change.

Visits and revisits

If repairs are not executed, or if they prove ineffective, then further inspections will be required. It may be that by that stage the matter is handled by some other member of the housing team, perhaps a maintenance manager, but nevertheless the housing manager needs to be aware of the activity.

At each subsequent inspection, the original schedule and report should be revised to show the change in conditions. This enables the tracking of each individual defect which can prove invaluable at a later date. Again, computerised systems can assist greatly with this tracking of repairs history.

CHAPTER 9

COURT PROCEEDINGS

Instructing an expert / Expert evidence and advice / Choice of expert / Housing manager's evidence / Compliance with orders

A court hearing can result in an order for works to be done, a money judgment of compensation payable and a legal resolution to a dispute on liability. In the course of proceedings both the facts and the interpretation of the law may be in dispute. Both of these can affect the liability for carrying out the repair as well as any payment of compensation for the failure to repair.

Some cases may be settled at the door of the court, but nevertheless the housing manager has to be equipped and ready to attend court and present her or his evidence to a judge. The majority of cases with which housing managers will deal are tried under civil law in the county courts. Some may go the High Court, but for disrepair this is rare.

Environmental Protection Act prosecutions are dealt with in the magistrates' court under the criminal justice system. Although the standard of proof is different and the rules regarding advance disclosure of evidence are less rigorous than in civil cases, these prosecutions can be dealt with on a quasi-civil basis, with advance discussions between the parties and their advisers minimising the costs of any hearing. See further A. Kilpatrick *Repairs and Maintenance*, ch. 10 pp. 133-134.

In any of these cases, the housing manager will be a lay witness of fact not an expert. Accordingly the same rules of conduct will apply as to any other witness in the case. Witnesses of fact are traditionally excluded from the trial until after they have given evidence. However, in both criminal and civil proceedings concerning housing disrepair, all witnesses are usually allowed into court unless specific objection is made.

Instructing an expert

The decision to instruct an expert needs to be made at the stage when the complaint is first received, and then reviewed at each successive stage. The following questions should be answered:
• Is there an adequately qualified/experienced staff member who can properly assess the complaints?
• Are the facts concerning the complaint clearly established from the point of view of both sides?
• Are the defects complained of clearly the liability of one side or the other?
• Are the required repairs clearly specified?
• Is the matter definitely going to be resolved without going to trial?

Only if all of these questions are answered in the affirmative can the appointment of an expert be excluded.

The time to appoint an expert will depend on when the answers to the questions above cease to be affirmative and stray into the negative, or even to "don't know".

It is false economy to allow a complaint to proceed towards litigation without assessing the merits of the case.

Expert evidence and advice

The role of an expert witness is different to that of a lay witness. The expert, unlike the lay witness, is required not only to deal with facts known to her or him, but also to express an opinion on the interpretation of those facts in the context of the case before the court. For this reason, the expert evidence presented to the court must be independent and unbiased (guidance on this is provided in the decision of Mr Justice Cresswell in *Ikarian Reefer* [1993] 2 Lloyd's Rep 68).

The duties and responsibilities of expert witnesses can be summarised as follows. An expert witness should:

- present evidence to the court which should be (and should be seen to be) the independent product of the expert uninfluenced as to form or content by the exigencies of litigation;
- provide independent assistance to the court by way of objective unbiased opinion in relation to matters within her or his expertise;
- never assume the role of advocate;
- state the facts or substance on which her or his opinion is based;
- not omit to consider material facts which detract

from the conclusion;
- make it clear when a particular question falls outside of her or his expertise;
- if insufficient research has been possible, state the opinion as provisional.

Expert advice, on the other hand, is opinion based on the facts presented which is given to the party on whose behalf the expert is instructed. This advice may include matters which are potentially damaging to the client's case.

The distinction between these roles is a delicate one and can be a very hard one for experts to tread. However, the duties imposed on expert witnesses mean that the damaging factors must be taken into account in the presentation of evidence to the court. In some well-publicised cases, experts have been criticised for straying from their expert witness role.

In *London & Leeds Estates v Paribas* (1993) 66 P & CR 218, CA an expert was ordered by the court to disclose his evidence from another case, which went to arbitration, on the basis that his approach was inconsistent. The court stated that an expert must resist any subconscious tendency to become a member of a team and as a result to proffer views unduly favourable to the position of the party instructing him.

In *Kenning v Eve Construction* [1995] 1 WLR 1189, the expert had written a report for disclosure and in a covering letter expressed views contrary to his client's case. The judge concluded that the party instructing the expert could either not call the expert at trial, and therefore exclude all his evidence, or if called, should disclose the whole of the expert's opinion, damaging or not to the client's case.

Choice of expert

In cases of housing disrepair, the criteria which should be the basis for selection of an expert are proven technical and legal experience as well as in giving evidence – and being right first time.

A thorough knowledge of the type of building under consideration is required together with a good understanding of the relevant law so that the opinions expressed on liability for a defect and/or the extent of repair can be accurately assessed.

Previous experience as an expert witness is a further criterion for selection. A successful track record will add to the expert's stature in the eyes of the court and will allow the instructing party to have confidence in the opinions expressed. The expert should have a record of being able to substantiate the opinions and report at trial. For this reason the expert may, on occasion, need to play devil's advocate in the investigative stage of the report so as to tease out facts which could affect the opinion or diagnosis. For example, there may have been inexcusable delay in carrying out a minor repair which would have prevented a greater defect. The running overflow from a defective ball-valve, requiring a simple and cheap repair, will in time cause dampness to the structure and possible fungal decay.

There will, of course, always be cases where facts are disclosed only at a late stage – sometimes even during the trial and these will affect the opinions expressed. For example, in cases of dampness where the combination of condensation and penetrating damp to the overall damp conditions must be assessed, the disclosure for the first time at trial by the tenant that a flueless gas heater has been used may significantly alter the balance between two competing explanations.

Housing manager's evidence

Witness statements must be prepared by both sides and exchanged before trial. At trial these statements will form the heart of the evidence given by each witness.

Keeping proper records and tracking events should mean that an effective statement can be prepared on the basis of that information. The statement will need to rehearse the history of the case, from the first complaint or notification of a defect through to the present stage. Later, a final statement may be confined to a particular area or time. Information for this will be drawn from the notes, reports and photographs prepared by the housing manager, as well as from records held on housing files. Photographs showing the general conditions will assist the court to form a view of the overall condition of the property. Close-ups of individual defects are often difficult to show and may require a higher level of photographic skill than is available (see also p. 76, above).

Compliance with orders

Any works to be executed as part of a court order should be executed methodically. The procedures described in chapter 8 give guidance on this.

Where genuine reasons cause delay in complying with a court order, for example, unforeseen works, refusal of access by the tenant, then the housing manager must be alert to the need either to agree with the tenant that the time allowed in the court order can be extended, or be prepared to return to court to obtain an extension. On potential penalties for failure see A. Kilpatrick *Repairs and Maintenance*, ch. 5 pp. 70-72.

If a return to court is necessary, the housing manager must attend fully equipped with all the reasons to justify the application. This may include letters and reports as well as personal evidence of the reasons for delay. Any extension of time should be sought prior to expiry.

CHAPTER 10

CONCLUSION

Achieving good value from the repairs executed can improve tenant satisfaction, reduce the pressures on housing managers, save money for the landlord and save on resources. To achieve good value, defects must be correctly diagnosed, the remedy identified and the remedial works executed in accordance with a pre-planned priority.

The application of ISO 9001 (BS 5750) for quality assurance in housing management is as yet not common, but this, coupled with the performance criteria set down by monitoring bodies and by statute, brings with it a real need to establish written procedures and to monitor both their implementation and the extent to which they work in practice.

Procedures, at least in the context of ISO 9001, need to be relevant and have operational credibility. Processes which are laudable but totally impractical for the staff who have to implement them are of little use. The inability to adhere to the process generates hybrid methods and encourages a formal and informal way of doing work. This duplication brings the strategic objective of a quality service into disrepute and defeats the aim of learning from a continuous review and improvement of the operational processes. The implementation of new procedures should be preceded by a thorough audit of the operations actually carried out by existing staff. Long-serving staff should be involved in the consultation.

By understanding that a defect is not necessarily only what can be seen, the housing manager will be able to assess whether what is visible is a symptom of a more serious or less serious defect than at first appears. This understanding enables informed judgements to be made on the type of repair required, its priority, and the implications for both the landlord and the occupants. The housing manager can more accurately relate the circumstances to the legal obligations of the landlord. This will enable the setting of priorities and monitoring of progress with an eye not just to the immediate efficient use of the repairs resources, but also to minimising expenditure of the limited funds on litigation.

APPENDIX I

Building diagrams

Fig. 1.1 Solid outer wall
    1.2 Cavity wall
    1.3 Blockwork

Fig. 2.1 Timber stud
      partition
      a. stud
      partitioning
      b. lath-and-
      plaster wall
    2.2 Blockwork
      partition

Fig 3.1 Timber plates
    3.2 Brick stepped
      footings
    3.3 Strip foundations
      a. concrete
      b. narrow strip
    3.4 Raft foundations
      a. flat raft
      b. wide toe raft
    3.5 Pile foundation

Fig. 4.1 Pitched roof
    4.2 Valley roof

Fig. 5.1 Metal flat roof
    5.2 Asphalt and felt
      coverings on
      a. timber roof
      b. concrete roof

Fig. 6.1 Timber upper
      floor
    6.2 Timber ground
      floor
    6.3 Solid ground
      floor

Fig. 7.1 Sliding sashes
    7.2 Casement
      windows
    7.3 Bow windows
    7.4 Bay windows
    7.5 Louvre windows
    7.6 Pivot windows

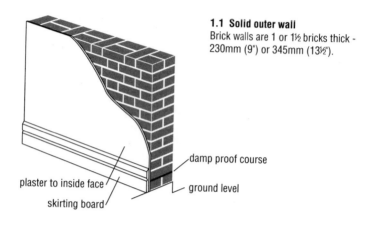

1.1 Solid outer wall
Brick walls are 1 or 1½ bricks thick - 230mm (9") or 345mm (13½").

damp proof course

ground level

plaster to inside face

skirting board

1.2 Cavity wall
Two independent leaves linked with metal ties with a cavity 50mm wide and is about 280mm thick overall. The outer leaf is usually brick. The inner leaf of bricks or blocks carries most of the load of floors and roof.

plaster to inside face

wall tie

damp proof course

ground level

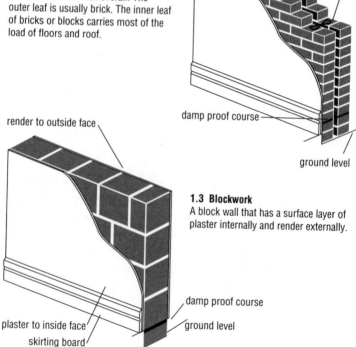

render to outside face

1.3 Blockwork
A block wall that has a surface layer of plaster internally and render externally.

damp proof course

ground level

plaster to inside face

skirting board

2.1 Timber stud partition

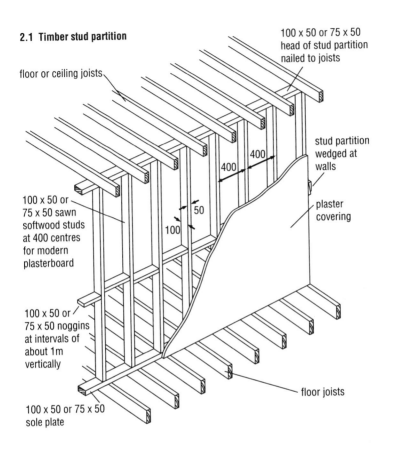

100 x 50 or 75 x 50 head of stud partition nailed to joists

floor or ceiling joists

400 400

stud partition wedged at walls

100 x 50 or 75 x 50 sawn softwood studs at 400 centres for modern plasterboard

50

100

plaster covering

100 x 50 or 75 x 50 noggins at intervals of about 1m vertically

100 x 50 or 75 x 50 sole plate

floor joists

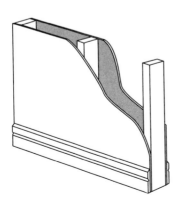

2.1a Stud partitioning

This common interior wall is made from a framework of timber studs. Today it is faced with plasterboard. The wall may, or may not, be load bearing.

2.1b Lath-and-plaster wall

Found in older houses. The plaster is about 25mm thick and mixed with horsehair to increase its strength. The plaster is bonded to horizontal laths of split timber nailed to the timber uprights. If the wall is load-bearing, it may have diagonal struts between the timber uprights.

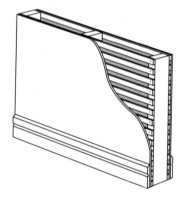

2.2 Blockwork partition

A block wall that has a surface layer of plaster.

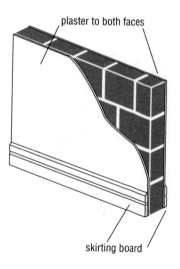

plaster to both faces

skirting board

3.1 Timber plates

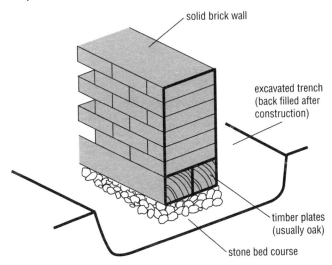

solid brick wall

excavated trench
(back filled after
construction)

timber plates
(usually oak)

stone bed course

3.2 Brick stepped footings

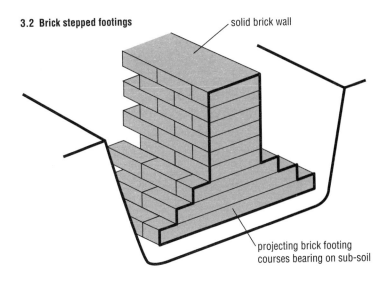

solid brick wall

projecting brick footing
courses bearing on sub-soil

3.3a Concrete strip foundations

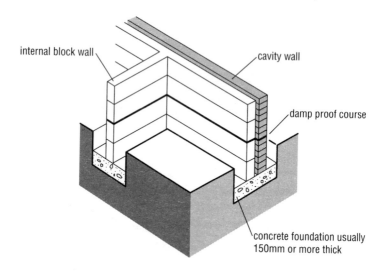

internal block wall

cavity wall

damp proof course

concrete foundation usually
150mm or more thick

3.3b Narrow strip foundations

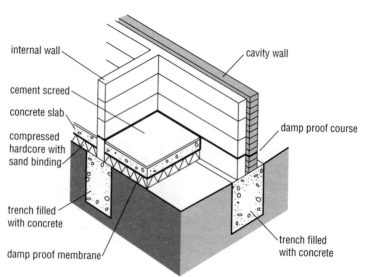

internal wall

cavity wall

cement screed

concrete slab

compressed
hardcore with
sand binding

damp proof course

trench filled
with concrete

trench filled
with concrete

damp proof membrane

3.4a Flat raft foundations

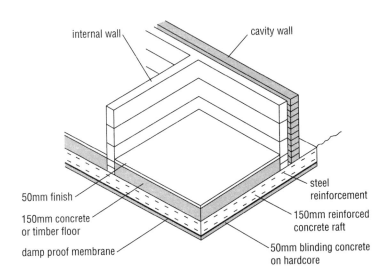

internal wall

cavity wall

50mm finish

150mm concrete
or timber floor

damp proof membrane

steel
reinforcement

150mm reinforced
concrete raft

50mm blinding concrete
on hardcore

3.4b Wide toe raft foundations

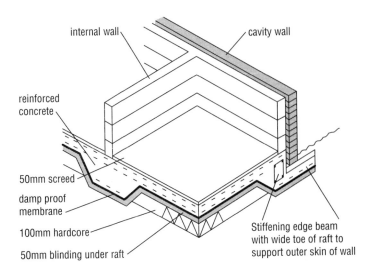

internal wall

cavity wall

reinforced
concrete

50mm screed

damp proof
membrane

100mm hardcore

50mm blinding under raft

Stiffening edge beam
with wide toe of raft to
support outer skin of wall

3.5 Pile foundation

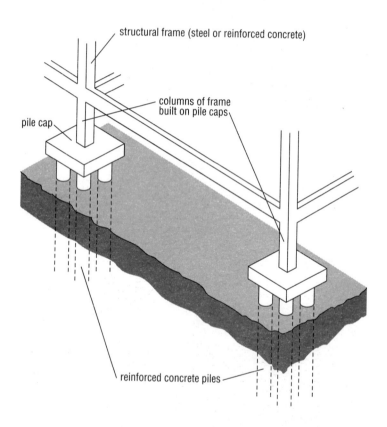

4.1 Pitched roof

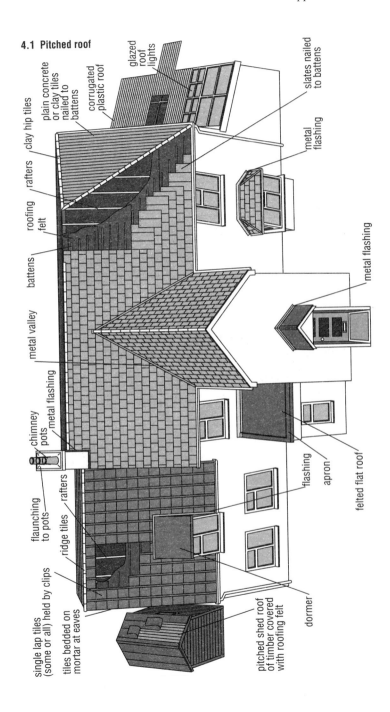

glazed roof lights

slates nailed to batten

plain concrete or clay tiles nailed to battens

corrugated plastic roof

clay hip tiles

metal flashing

rafters

roofing felt

battens

metal flashing

metal valley

metal flashing

chimney pots

metal flashing

flaunching to pots

ridge tiles

rafters

flashing

apron

felted flat roof

single lap tiles (some or all) held by clips

tiles bedded on mortar at eaves

pitched shed roof of timber covered with roofing felt

dormer

4.2 Valley roof

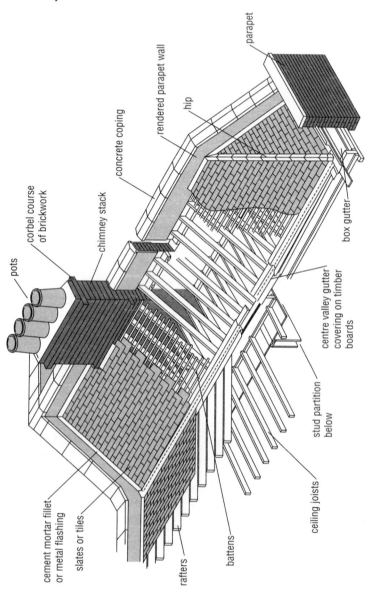

parapet

rendered parapet wall

hip

concrete coping

chimney stack

corbel course
of brickwork

pots

box gutter

centre valley gutter
covering on timber
boards

stud partition
below

ceiling joists

cement mortar fillet
or metal flashing

slates or tiles

rafters

battens

5.1 Metal flat roof

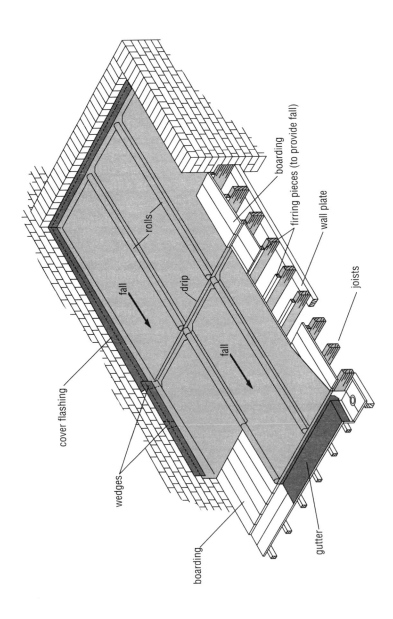

5.2a Timber roof

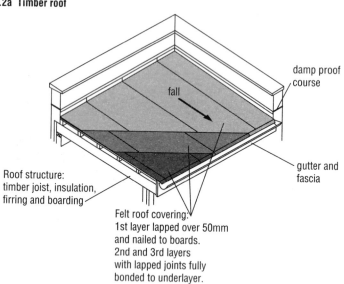

damp proof course

fall

gutter and fascia

Roof structure:
timber joist, insulation,
firring and boarding

Felt roof covering:
1st layer lapped over 50mm
and nailed to boards.
2nd and 3rd layers
with lapped joints fully
bonded to underlayer.

5.2b Concrete roof

roof screed primed
with bitumen

verge

Felt roof covering:
initial bond by bitumen
with perimeter 450mm
wide with 150mm vents
and strip sticking.
1st layer of roofing
felt part bonded.
2nd and 3rd layer of
felt fully bonded.

cavity wall

Verge:

felt turned over verge
fillet and nailed to fascia

min. 50mm

three layers of
bitumen roofing felt

fascia board

screed

cavity insulation fill
up to roof level

concrete roof

6.1 Timber upper floor

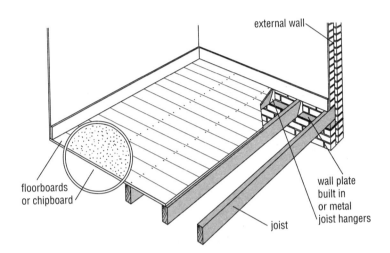

external wall

floorboards
or chipboard

wall plate
built in
or metal
joist hangers

joist

6.2 Timber ground floor

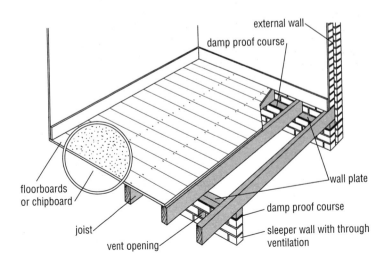

external wall

damp proof course

floorboards
or chipboard

joist

vent opening

wall plate

damp proof course

sleeper wall with through
ventilation

6.3 Solid ground floor

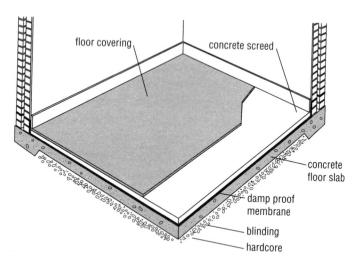

floor covering

concrete screed

concrete floor slab

damp proof membrane

blinding

hardcore

7.1 Sliding sashes

These slide up and down, but more modern types particularly with plastic frames may slide from side to side. Traditional timber sash windows are operated by weights attached to sash cords. Modern designs have spring-action spiral sash balances. Some tilt inwards for easy cleaning.

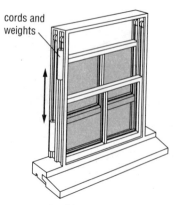

cords and weights

traditional wooden sash

plastic sash (in a wooden sub-frame)

7.2 Casement windows

Casements open on hinges. They usually open outwards. There may also be one or more fixed panes. Side-hinged casements are usually large, while top-hinged casements are small.

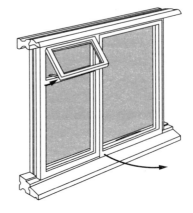

7.3 Bow windows

Usually multiple casements made to form a shallow curve.

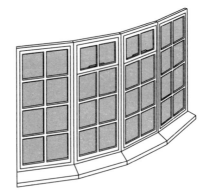

7.4 Bay windows

Most bay windows are made with stone or brick piers projecting beyond the line of the wall, and fitted with sliding sashes. But a bay window can also be made with a series of casement or sash windows joined together.

structural posts at corners

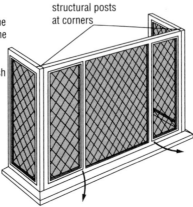

7.5 Louvre windows

Horizontal slats of glass attached to the frame at each side can be adjusted to control ventilation.

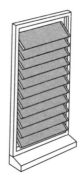

7.6 Pivot windows

Projected windows.
A sliding action moves the bottom of the window outwards while the top rail slides down in channels in each side of the frame.

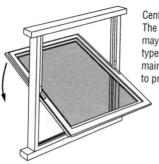

Centre pivot.
The window pivots at its mid-point, and may also have a fixed pane. Some types are reversible for cleaning and maintenance. Safety catches are fitted to prevent accidental rotation.

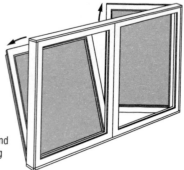

Tilt-and-turn.
These open inwards at the top, for ventilation without a security risk, and also open from one side for cleaning and maximum ventilation.

APPENDIX II

Diagnosing building defects: "following the trail"

"Following the trail" is a term taken from surveying practice. It is often referred to in litigation and concerns surveyors' failure to observe or adequately interpret "trigger" defects.

This Appendix does not give the reader all the possible options which could cause or result from each trigger defect as these are available from other sources, including computer information programmes. It does give an example of the process and sets out the first few questions to reduce these options to a manageable number.

Diagnosing Building Defects

Trigger Defect	Initial Options of Cause/Result	Question/Answer	Options Remaining
Water on window frame internally	Condensation	Running water on glass?	Yes – condensation No – water penetration
	Water penetration	Holes around window?	Yes – water penetration No – condensation
Damp patch on ceiling	Water penetration	Roof over?	No – plumbing leak Yes – roof leak
	Plumbing leak	Rooms or loft above?	Yes – plumbing leak No – other water source
	Condensation	Loft above?	Yes – possible condensation from within roofspace No – other water source
Damp solid ground floor	Rising damp	Distinct pattern, uniformly damp, high moisture meter readings more noticeable at perimeter	No – leakage or condensation Yes – rising damp
	Condensation	General dampness, low moisture meter readings, dampest under impervious floor coverings	No – leakage or rising damp Yes – condensation

Diagnosing Building Defects

Trigger Defect	Initial Options of Cause/Result	Question/Answer	Options Remaining
Damp solid ground floor	Leakage	Distinct pattern, uniformly damp, high moisture meter readings, area affected in straight line/following pipe runs	No – condensation or rising damp Yes – leakage
Dampness to walls at lowest floor level	Rising damp	Distinct pattern, uniformly damp, high moisture meter readings, clear cut off to almost nil moisture meter reading	No – condensation Yes – rising damp
Rising damp	Dampness rising from the ground in the wall	Is there a damp-proof course in the wall?	Yes – bridging or lateral penetration or contaminated plaster No – rising damp
	Dampness rising from the ground in the floor	Is there a damp-proof membrane in the floor?	Yes – bridging or lateral penetration No – rising damp
	Dampness rising from the ground in the wall and floor	Is there a link between the damp-proof course and the damp-proof membrane?	Yes – contaminated plaster No – bridging or lateral penetration

Diagnosing Building Defects

Trigger Defect	Initial Options of Cause/Result	Question/Answer	Options Remaining
Rising Damp	Dampness penetrating from high ground	Is the floor below ground level?	Yes – bridging or lateral penetration No – contaminated plaster
Damp patch on a wall	Water penetration	Is it an outside wall?	Yes – water penetration No – leakage
		Is there a leaking rainwater pipe or gutter outside?	Yes – likely cause No – other discrete cause
	Condensation in a chimney	If it is on a chimney breast, is the flue capped and swept?	Yes – condensation or other source No – water from flue and/or dampened debris on chimney throat
	Condensation in the room	Is there mould growth?	Yes – clean water source, e.g. internal plumbing or condensation No – contaminated water source, e.g. ground water

Diagnosing Building Defects

Trigger Defect	Initial Options of Cause/Result	Question Answer	Options Remaining
Window does not operate fully	Jammed shut	Has it been painted?	Yes – stuck with paint No – swollen/rotten or rusted
	Rotten/rusted	If a timber window, is it rotten, or if a metal window, rusted?	Yes – repair window No – other defects

CUMULATIVE INDEX

Abandoned premises
conditions for security of
tenure, 1:53-54
notice to quit, 1:110-111
Absence from premises
conditions for security of
tenure, 1:48-49
prolonged, 1:48-49
Accelerated procedure
possession proceedings,
1:108, 4:114
Access
neighbouring land, to,
5:115-116
Accident
inevitable, as defence to
private nuisance action,
3:21-22
Accommodation
disabled, for, 1:80
elderly, for, 1:19-20
employment related, 1:76-77,
4:41-42
essential for job, 1:24-25
homeless persons, for, 1:34-35
1:42
hostel. *See* Hostel
accommodation
information about
applications, 2:58-59
job mobility, 1:35-36
pending works, 1:37, 1:77-78,
4:40-41

shared, 1:45-46
sheltered, 1:81
special needs, 1:80-81
tied, 1:24, 1:88, 4:34-35
Adjournment of possession
proceedings. *See* Possession
proceedings
Affidavit
evidence, 4:71-72
meaning, 4:154
summary possession, 4:116
Agent
repairs,
liability for, 5:10-11
notice relating to, 5:33-35
Agreement
surrender, to, 1:125
tenancy,
assured tenancy, 2:54-55
breach of, as ground for
possession, 3:60-61
changing terms of, 2:50-55
covenant, meaning, 2:99
fixed term tenancy, 2:54
harassment, prevention of,
3:84-87
**inspection of disrepair,
preparing for, 6:73**
periodic tenancy, 2:54-55
secure tenancy, 2:50-54
termination of, 4:8-13
Agricultural holdings
tenancy of, 1:37, 1:40

Entries in this volume appear in bold.
1. *Security of Tenure* 2. *Tenants' Rights* 3. *Nuisance and Harassment*
4. *Presenting Possession Proceedings* 5. *Repairs and Maintenance*
6. *Dealing with Disrepair*

Agricultural land
  assured tenancy, exception to,
    1:40
Allocation of housing
  information about, 2:57-58
  secure tenants, information
    to, 2:62
  suitable alternative
    accommodation, 1:91-92
Ancillary rights of tenants
  summary, 2:3-4
Animals
  disease carrying, 6:55
  private nuisance, as, 3:16
Annoyance
  assured tenant, grounds for
    possession against, 1:88
  evidence, 1:72
  letter to tenant causing, 1:133
  meaning, 1:71
  neighbours, complaints from,
    1:72
  nuisance and, 3:61-63
  possession proceedings,
    generally, 4:106-109
  proof of annoyance, 4:39
  return date, 4:110
  undertakings, 4:110-112
  witness statement, 4:110
  secure tenant, grounds for
    possession against, 1:70-73
  those who live with tenant,
    caused by, 1:71
  visitors, caused by, 1:71
Appeals
  compensation orders, relating
    to, 5:102
  environmental protection,
    relating to, 5:102
  possession procedure,
    4:136-137
Application to set aside
  possession order, 1:123-124
Asbestos
  complaints relating to, 5:59-60
  removal contractors, 6:52-53

  use of, 6:52-53
Asphalt
  description of, 6:34-35
Assignment
  assured tenancy, of, 2:44-46
  enforcement of right of,
    2:28-29
  exchange, by way of,
    consent, grounds for
      refusing, 2:36-39
    generally, 2:35
    landlord's written consent,
      2:35-36
  generally, 1:8, 2:31
  potential successor, to, 2:32-33
  proof of, 2:33-34
  secure tenancy, of,
    exchange, assignment by
      way of, 2:35-39
    generally, 2:32
    mutual exchange, 2:35-39
    potential successor, to,
      2:32-33
    proof of assignment, 2:33-34
    property transfer order,
      2:32
    successor assignee, seeking
      possession against, 2:34-35
  statutory periodic tenancy,
    2:46
Assured shorthold tenancy
  county court, accelerated
    procedure in, 1:108
  features, 1:106-107
  hostel accommodation, 1:116
  nature of, 1:105
  new shorthold, 1:107
  possession, 1:107, 4:113-114
  probationary tenancy, 3:44-45
  purposes, 1:106
Assured tenancy
  assignment of, 2:44-2:46
  change of landlord, 1:42
  conditions, 1:44
  consultation with assured
    tenants, 2:75-77

Entries in this volume appear in bold.
1. *Security of Tenure* 2. *Tenants' Rights* 3. *Nuisance and Harassment*
4. *Presenting Possession Proceedings* 5. *Repairs and Maintenance*
6. *Dealing with Disrepair*

exceptions,
  agricultural holdings,
    tenancy of, 1:40
  agricultural land, tenancy
    of, 1:40
  business tenancy, 1:40
  crown tenancy, 1:41
  exempt landlord, 1:41
  high rateable values,
    tenancy of premises
      with, 1:39
  holiday lets, 1:40
  homeless person, 1:42
  licensed premises, 1:40
  long leaseholder, 1:40
  resident landlord, 1:41
  student lets, 1:40
  tenancy created before
    commencement of Act,
      1:39
  tenants with other classes
    of protection, 1:41
forfeiture of, 1:66
generally, 1:29
lodgers, 2:47
meaning, 2:99, 3:99, 4:154
nature of, 1:38-39
possession, grounds of,
  annoyance, 1:88
  breach of term of tenancy,
    1:87
  deterioration of dwelling-
    house, 1:88
  discretionary grounds,
    1:86-88
  furniture, deterioration of,
    1:88
  generally, 1:83
  holiday letting out of
    season, 1:84
  inherited tenancy, 1:85-86
  landlord's works, 1:84-85
  mandatory grounds, 1:84-86
  ministers of religion, 1:84
  mortgaged property, 1:84
  nuisance, 1:88

rent arrears, 1:86, 1:87
returning home owner, 1:84
specimen form of order,
  4:150-151
student letting, 1:84
suitable alternative
  accommodation, 1:87
tied accommodation, 1:88
rights of tenants,
  generally, 2:5-6
  tenants' guarantees, 2:6-7
shorthold. *See* Assured
  shorthold tenancy
subletting, 2:46
succession,
  common law, at, 2:23-24
  contractual succession
    clauses, 2:26-30
  generally, 2:23
  Housing Act 1988, under,
    2:24-25
  who is successor, 2:25
  who succeeds, 2:25
suitable alternative
  accommodation,
    comparison with local
      authority practice, 1:94
    furniture, 1:94
    generally, 1:93
    local authority certificate,
      1:93
    location, 1:95
    reluctant tenants, 1:94-95
    suitability, 1:93-94
tenancy agreement, 2:54-55

Basements
  damp-proofing, 6:19
Behaviour of perpetrator
  private nuisance and, 3:18
Bituminous materials
  description of, 6:34-35
Breach
  other term, of, reasonableness
    and, 1:102-103
  repairs, relating to. *See*

Entries in this volume appear in bold.
1. *Security of Tenure* 2. *Tenants' Rights* 3. *Nuisance and Harassment*
4. *Presenting Possession Proceedings* 5. *Repairs and Maintenance*
6. *Dealing with Disrepair*

Repairs and maintenance
5:60-63

Brick

description of, 6:26

external walls,

cavity brickwork, 6:10

solid brickwork, 6:10

footings, 6:12

Building

Act of 1984, local authority
powers under, 5:105

diagnosing defects, 6:163-167

diagrams, 6:147-162

disrepair. *See* Disrepair

repairs. *See* Repairs and
maintenance

Burden of proof
meaning, 4:154

Bushes

disrepair caused by, 6:55-56

Business tenancy
assured tenancy, exclusion
from, 1:40

secure tenancy, exclusion
from, 1:38

Camera

**inspection of disrepair, use
for, 6:76**

Causation
compensation awards,
assessment of, 5:101-102

Change of landlord
assured tenancy, 1:42
secure tenancy, 1:42

Charity
secure tenant, grounds for
possession against, 1:79

**Chartered Institute of Housing
Housing Management
Standards Manual, 6:122**

Climate. *See* Temperature and
climate

Closing speeches
possession proceedings, 4:81

Cockroaches
complaints relating to,

private nuisance, as, 3:17

Codes of practice

**disrepair, priorities in dealing
with, 6:119-120**

Cohabitees
rights of, 1:111-112

Commencing possession
proceedings. *See*
Possession proceedings

Commission for Racial Equality
racial harassment, meaning,
3:70

Committal proceedings
meaning, 4:154

Committees
representation on, 2:76-77

Common law
meaning, 3:99
public nuisance, 3:23-24
succession at, 2:10, 2:23-24

Common parts

damage to, 1:74

**inspection of disrepair,
preparing for, 6:73**

repair, liability for, 5:22-24

Compensation
improvements, for, 5:125
orders,
appeals, 5:102
causation, 5:101-102
levels of compensation,
5:101
power to make, 5:100-101

Complaints
damp, relating to,
condensation damp, 5:56-57
generally, 5:53
penetrating damp, 5:53-55
rising damp, 5:55-56
neighbours, from, 1:72
nuisance, relating to, 3:39-40

Compulsory competitive
tendering
local authority, by, 2:89
nuisance and, 3:43-44

Entries in this volume appear in bold.
1. *Security of Tenure* 2. *Tenants' Rights* 3. *Nuisance and Harassment*
4. *Presenting Possession Proceedings* 5. *Repairs and Maintenance*
6. *Dealing with Disrepair*

Concrete
   description of, 6:30
   reinforced,
      foundations, 6:13
      frame, 6:21
Condensation
   complaints relating to, 5:56-57
   from inside, 6:45
   interstitial, 6:46
Conditions for security of
   tenure
   abandonment, 1:53-54
   assured tenancy, 1:44
   dwelling-house, 1:44
   gaining possession, 1:55
   generally, 1:43
   let as separate dwelling,
      meaning, 1:45-46
      separate, meaning, 1:45
      shared accomodation,
         1:45-46
   lodgers,
      generally, 1:51
      illegal occupation, 1:52-53
      loss of security of tenure,
         1:51-52
   residence condition, 1:43,
      1:46-51
   secure tenancy, 1:43-44
   subletting,
      generally, 1:51
      illegal occupation, 1:52-53
      loss of security of tenure,
         1:51-52
   surrender, 1:53-54
   use as home,
      absence from premises,
         1:48-49
      prolonged absence, 1:48-49
      residence condition, 1:46-51
      two homes, 1:49-51
Consent order
   possession proceedings,
      4:126-129
Consolidation
   meaning, 4:154

possession proceedings,
   4:51-52
Construction materials. *See*
   Materials of construction
Consultation
   assured tenants, with,
      2:75-77
   committees, representation on,
      generally, 2:77
      housing associations,
         2:78
      local authorities, 2:77
   housing action trust,
      declaration of, 2:93
   housing association,
      sale tenanted to, 2:92
      sale with vacant
         possession, 2:93
   local authority,
      redevelopment by, 2:94
   other forms, 2:77-79
   rent levies for tenants' funds,
      2:79
   secure tenants, with,
      acquisition by new
         landlord, 2:74-75
      basic requirement, 2:65
      generally, 2:65
      housing action trust, 2:73-74
      large scale voluntary
         transfers, 2:71-72
      managing agents, use of,
         2:69-71
      matters requiring
         consultation, 2:66-69
      method of consultation,
         2:65-66
      other duties, 2:69-75
      outcome of consultation,
         2:69
      redevelopment scheme,
         declaration of, 2:72-73
   tenants' organisations,
      funding for, 2:78-79
   See also Information
Contingency fees

Entries in this volume appear in bold.
1. *Security of Tenure* 2. *Tenants' Rights* 3. *Nuisance and Harassment*
4. *Presenting Possession Proceedings* 5. *Repairs and Maintenance*
6. *Dealing with Disrepair*

environmental protection,
  relating to, 5:103-104
Contract
  breach of, limitation periods,
    5:78
  repairing obligation of social
    landlord. *See* Repairs and
    maintenance
Contractual succession clauses
  alternative approach, 2:29-30
  enforceability of right of
    assignment, 2:28-29
  generally, 2:26
  housing association, 2:26-27
  local authority, 2:27-28, 2:29
Costs
  environmental protection,
    relating to, 5:102-103
  possession proceedings. *See*
    Possession proceedings
  repair, litigation relating to,
    5:2-3, 5:102-103
Counterclaims
  disrepair, for, 1:100-101
  set-off and, 5:82-83
County court
  accelerated procedure in,
    1:108, 4:114
  application to set aside,
    1:123-124
  rules, 3:3
  squatters, procedure relating
    to, 1:113
  suspended order, powers
    relating to, 1:120-121
  trespassers, procedure
    relating to, 1:113
Court
  choice of, possession
    proceedings, 4:13-14
  commencing possession
    proceedings, 4:13-14
  county. *See* County court
  disrepair, dealing with. *See*
    Disrepair
  repairs, proceedings relating

to. *See* Repairs and
  maintenance
Covenants
  meaning, 3:99-100, 4:155
  quiet enjoyment, for, breach
    of, 5:38, 5:46-47
  right to buy, harassment and,
    3:87
Cross-examination
  meaning, 4:155
  possession proceedings,
    4:79-80
Crown Prosecution Service
  (CPS)
  criminal proceedings, 3:78
Crown tenancy
  assured tenancy, exclusion
    from, 1:41

Damage
  private nuisance and, 3:18
Damages
  general, 5:73-76
  interest, 5:77
  landlord's remedy for breach,
    5:111-112
  redecoration, for, 5:76-77
  repairing obligations, failure
    to comply with, 5:71-77
  special, 5:72-73
Damp
  complaints relating to, 5:53-57
  condensation, 5:56-57
  lateral penetration, 6:39-40
  **moisture generation by users,
    6:54**
  moisture meter, 6:75-76
  penetrating, 5:53-55
  rising, 5:55-56, 6:38-39
  **salts and residual dampness,
    6:42-43**
Damp-proofing
  basements, 6:19
  bridging, 6:41
  generally, 6:18
  ground floors, 6:19

Entries in this volume appear in bold.
1. *Security of Tenure* 2. *Tenants' Rights* 3. *Nuisance and Harassment*
4. *Presenting Possession Proceedings* 5. *Repairs and Maintenance*
6. *Dealing with Disrepair*

remedial, 6:40-41
walls, 6:18
Dampness. *See* Damp
Dangerous premises
  private nuisance, as, 3:17
Dealing with disrepair. *See*
  Disrepair
Deceased tenant
  successor, as, 2:19-21
Deception
  tenancy obtained by,
    1:75-76
Decorations
  redecoration,
    damages for, 5:76-77
    repairing obligation and,
      5:31
Defective premises
  notice, 5:41-43
  premises, meaning, 5:43-44
  relevant defect, meaning,
    5:40-41
  social landlord's non-
    contractual liabilities, 5:38,
    5:39-44, 5:47-48
Defects. *See* Disrepair
Defences
  possession proceedings. *See*
    Possession proceedings
  private nuisance, action for,
    generally, 3:21
    ignorance, 3:22
    inevitable accident, 3:21-22
    statutory authorisation,
      3:22
Deliberate action
  private nuisance, as, 3:17
Deterioration
  furniture, of, 1:73-75, 1:88
  possession proceedings,
    4:39-40
  premises, of, 1:73-75, 1:88
Development
  home being redeveloped,
    letter relating to, 1:133-134
  land, 1:32-34, 4:35-36

meaning, 1:33
Diary of incidents
  form, 1:143
Direct action
  rent,
    repairs, use to pay for,
      5:84-85
    set-off against, 5:81
  set-off,
    counterclaims, and, 5:82-83
    rent, against, 5:81
Directions
  meaning, 4:155
  possession proceedings. *See*
    Possession proceedings
Disabled person
  accommodation for, 1:80
Discharge
  suspended possession order,
    of, 1:122
Disclosure
  exempt information, 2:59
Discovery
  meaning, 4:155
  possession proceedings. *See*
    Possession proceedings
Discretionary payments
  local authority, by, 5:125-126
Disease
  insects carrying, 6:50-51
Disputes
  management, 2:87-88
Disrepair
  animals, disease carrying, 6:55
  assessing priorities,
    Chartered Institute of
      Housing Standards, 6:122
    codes of practice, 6:119-120
    general factors, 6:117-119
    individual basis, 6:117
    planned maintenance,
      6:122-124
    statutory obligations,
      6:119
    strategic basis, 6:117
    tenants' guarantee, 6:120

Entries in this volume appear in bold.
1. *Security of Tenure* 2. *Tenants' Rights* 3. *Nuisance and Harassment*
4. *Presenting Possession Proceedings* 5. *Repairs and Maintenance*
6. *Dealing with Disrepair*

tenants' right to repair,
6:121
value for money, 6:127-128
wholesale redevelopment
or rehabilitation,
6:124-127
building diagrams, 6:147-162
bushes, 6:55-56
compliance with orders,
6:142-143
counterclaims for, 1:100-101
court proceedings,
choice of expert, 6:141-142
compliance with orders,
6:142-143
expert evidence and
advice, 6:139-140
generally, 6:137-138
housing manager's
evidence, 6:142
instructing expert, 6:138-139
dealing with,
conclusion, 6:144-145
court proceedings. *See*
court proceedings, *above*
follow-up action. *See*
follow-up action, *below*
housing stock. *See* Housing
stock
inspection. *See* Inspection
of disrepair
materials of construction.
See Materials of
construction
priorities. *See* priorities,
below
reporting. *See* reporting,
below
diagnosing building defects,
6:163-167
enemies of health buildings,
animals, 6:55
bushes, 6:55-56
climate, 6:56-58
fungi, 6:47-49
generally, 6:36-37

hazardous materials,
6:52-54
insects, 6:49-51
metals, 6:51-52
non-traditional buildings,
6:59-61
plants, 6:55-56
refuse, 6:55
sulphates, 6:46
temperature, 6:56-58
trees, 6:55-56
underground threats, 6:58
users, 6:54
water, 6:37-46
evidence,
expert, 6:139-140
housing manager, of, 6:142
expert,
choice of, 6:141-142
evidence and advice,
6:139-140
instructing, 6:138-139
external advice, 6:116
follow-up action,
generally, 6:129
longer-term action,
6:135-136
monitoring performance,
6:130-131
monitoring short-term
repairs, 6:136
redecoration, 6:132-133
revisits, 6:136
tenants' satisfaction
surveys, 6:131-132
variations of works,
6:133-134
visits, 6:136
fungi,
dry rot, 6:47-48
generally, 6:46
moulds, 6:49
wet rot, 6:48-49
hazardous materials,
asbestos, 6:52-53
glass fibre, 6:53

Entries in this volume appear in bold.
1. *Security of Tenure* 2. *Tenants' Rights* 3. *Nuisance and Harassment*
4. *Presenting Possession Proceedings* 5. *Repairs and Maintenance*
6. *Dealing with Disrepair*

radon gas, 6:53-54
urea-formaldehyde foam,
     6:53
housing manager,
   court proceedings,
      evidence at, 6:142
   preparing for inspection,
      6:65-67
housing stock,
   non-traditional. *See* Non-
      traditional housing stock
   traditional. *See* Traditional
      housing stock
insects,
   disease carrying, 6:51-52
   just unpleasant, 6:51
   wood-boring, 6:49-50
inspection. *See* Inspection of
   disrepair
instructing expert, 6:138-139
longer-term action,
   generally, 6:135
   monitoring short-term
      repairs, 6:136
   revisits, 6:136
   visits, 6:136
materials of construction. *See*
   Materials of construction
metals, 6:51-52
monitoring,
   management systems,
      6:130-131
   performance, 6:130-131
   short-term repairs, 6:136
non-traditional housing stock,
   failures in, 6:59-61
   generally, 6:20-21
   high rise, 6:60-61
   large panel systems, 6:21,
      6:59-60
   modern timber-frame, 6:22,
      6:61
   no-fines, 6:22
   prefabricated buildings, 6:59
   steel and reinforced
      concrete frame, 6:21

orders, compliance with,
   6:142-143
plants, 6:55-56
possession proceedings,
   4:92-93
post-inspection practice. *See*
   Inspection of disrepair
priorities,
   assessing, 6:117-128
   external advice, 6:116
   generally, 6:115-116
   specification for repairs,
      6:116-117
redecoration, 6:132-133
refuse, 6:55
reporting,
   core section, 6:106-111
   customers, 6:104
   findings, 6:104-105
   format, 6:106-114
   generally, 6:103
   landlord's liability,
      6:113-114
   record note, 6:112-113
   reference to further action,
      6:114
   schedule of defects and
      repairs, 6:107-111
   supplementary sections,
      6:112
   tenant's liability, 6:114
short-term repairs, 6:136
specification for repairs,
   6:116-117
sulphates, 6:46
temperature and climate,
   drought, 6:56-57
   frost, 6:57
   snow, 6:57
   sun, 6:58
tenants,
   guarantee of, 6:120
   right to repair, 6:121
   satisfaction surveys,
      6:131-132
traditional housing stock. *See*

Entries in this volume appear in bold.
1. *Security of Tenure* 2. *Tenants' Rights* 3. *Nuisance and Harassment*
4. *Presenting Possession Proceedings* 5. *Repairs and Maintenance*
6. *Dealing with Disrepair*

Traditional housing stock
trees, 6:55-56
underground threats, 6:58
users, problems caused by,
  generally, 6:54
    moisture generation, 6:54
variations of works, 6:133-134
water,
  above ground, **6:43**
  construction, from, **6:46**
  dampness from ground,
    6:38-43
  from above, **6:44-45**
  from inside, **6:45-46**
  generally, **6:37-38**
  See also Repairs and
    maintenance
Divorce
  property transfer order, 2:32
Do-It-Yourself
  inspection of disrepair,
  6:99-100
Drains
  blocked, as private nuisance,
    3:17
  local authority, powers of,
    5:105
Drought
  disrepair caused by, 6:56-57
Dwelling-house
  deterioration of, 1:73-75, 1:88
  let as separate dwelling,
    meaning, 1:45-46
    separate, meaning, 1:45
    shared accommodation,
      1:45-46
  meaning, 1:44

Elderly
  accommodation for, 1:19-20
Employee
  accommodation essential for
    job, 1:24-25
  non-housing property
    required for, 1:80
  rights of, 1:25-28

secure tenancy, exclusion
  from, 1:32
service occupier, 1:24
service tenant, 1:24
tied accommodation, 1:24
Employment
  accommodation related to,
    1:76-77, 4:41-42
Enemies of healthy buildings.
  See **Disrepair**
Enforcement
  assignment, right of, 2:28-29
  injunction, through, 5:115
  possession order, of, 4:126
  tenants' guarantee, relating
    to, 2:6-7
Entry
  repairs, for, 5:114-116
Environmental health officers
  nuisance, powers relating to,
    3:29, 3:49
  possession proceedings,
    evidence at, 4:72-73
Environmental protection
  Act of 1990, 5:91-104
  action by tenant,
    generally, 5:94
    person aggrieved, 5:94-95
    person responsible, 5:95-99
  appeals, 5:102
  compensation orders,
    appeals, 5:102
    causation, 5:101-102
    generally, 5:100-101
    levels of compensation,
      5:101
  contingency fees, 5:103-104
  costs, 5:102-103
  local authority duty to
    residents, 5:93-94
  procedure, 5:99-100
  residents, local authority
    duty to, 5:93-94
  statutory nuisance,
    circumstances amounting
      to, 5:91-92

Entries in this volume appear in bold.
1. *Security of Tenure* 2. *Tenants' Rights* 3. *Nuisance and Harassment*
4. *Presenting Possession Proceedings* 5. *Repairs and Maintenance*
6. *Dealing with Disrepair*

individual 'person
aggrieved', action by,
3:28-29
local authority, action by,
3:26-28
nature of nuisance, 5:93
prejudicial to health, 5:92-93
required action under Act,
3:26-29
Estate redevelopment
consultation on declaration
of scheme, 2:72-73
generally, 2:91
housing action trust,
declaration of, 2:93-94
housing association,
local authority
development,
combination with, 2:95
sale tenanted to, 2:92-93
sale with vacant possession
to, 2:93
local authority,
housing association
development,
combination with, 2:95
redevelopment by, 2:94-95
Eviction, protection from
abandoned premises,
1:110-111
generally, 1:108
notice to quit, 1:108
period of notice, 1:109
service, 1:110
Evidence
annoyance, of, 1:72
expert,
disrepair, dealing with,
6:139-140
possession proceedings,
4:72-74
repairs, proceedings
relating to, 5:133-134
harassment, of, 3:88
hearsay, meaning, 4:156
in chief, meaning, 4:155

nuisance, of,
investigation of, 3:41-43
noise nuisance, 3:42-43
private investigator, use of,
3:42
secure tenant, grounds for
possession against, 1:72
possession proceedings. *See*
Possession proceedings
repairs and maintenance,
relating to,
experts' evidence, 5:133-134
generally, 5:129-131
housing manager as
witness, 5:132-133
specific performance, claim
for, 5:69-70
Ex parte
meaning, 3:100, 4:155
Exchange
assignment by way of,
consent, grounds for
refusing, 2:36-39
generally, 2:35
landlord's written consent,
2:35-36
mutual, 2:35-39
premium, at, 1:76
Exclusive possession
tenant and licensee
distinguished, 1:16-17
Exempt landlord
secure tenancy, relating to,
1:41
Expert evidence
disrepair, dealing with,
choice of expert, 6:141-142
instructing expert,
6:138-139
role of expert, 6:139-140
possession proceedings,
4:72-74
repairs, proceedings relating
to, 5:133-134
Express terms
implied terms conflicting

Entries in this volume appear in bold.
1. *Security of Tenure* 2. *Tenants' Rights* 3. *Nuisance and Harassment*
4. *Presenting Possession Proceedings* 5. *Repairs and Maintenance*
6. *Dealing with Disrepair*

with, 5:22
repairing obligation, relating
   to, 5:16-18
Exterior
   meaning, 5:14
   repairing obligation, 5:12-14

Fault
   nuisance based on, 5:50
Feasibility study
   full, 2:85-86
   initial, 2:84-85
Felt
   description of, 6:34-35
Financial incentives
   repair,
      costs of litigation, 5:2-3
      reasons for, 5:2-3
Fixed term tenancy
   forfeiture, 1:62-66
   meaning, 2:100, 4:155
   status of tenant, 1:7-8
   succession, 2:22
   tenancy agreement, 2:54-55
Floors
   above ground level, 6:16-17
   boards, 6:18
   damp-proofing, 6:19
   diagrams, 6:159-160
   ground,
      damp-proofing, 6:19
      solid, 6:17
      timber, 6:17
   sheets, 6:18
   solid ground floors, 6:17
   timber ground floors, 6:17
Forfeiture
   assured tenancy, of, 1:66
   fixed term tenancy, 1:62-66
   notice, 1:63-64
   provision for, 1:63
   re-entry, right of, 1:63
   relief from, 1:64-65
   rent arrears, action based on,
      1:65
   secure tenancy, of, 1:65

waiver, 1:64
Forms
   possession proceedings,
      4:143-153
Foundations
   brick footings, 6:12
   diagrams, 6:152-154
   piling, 6:13
   raft, 6:13
   reinforced concrete, 6:13
   strip, 6:12
   timber plates, 6:12
Freehold
   long leaseholder's right to
      acquire, 1:6-7
Frost
   disrepair caused by, 6:57
Funding
   rent levies for tenants' funds,
      2:79
   tenants' organisations, for,
      2:78-79
Fungi
   disrepair caused by, 6:47-49
   dry rot, 6:47-48
   moulds, 6:49
   wet rot, 6:48-49
Furniture
   deterioration of, 1:73-75, 1:88
   suitable alternative
      accommodation, in, 1:94
Further action. See Possession
   proceedings
Further and better particulars
   meaning, 4:155-156
   possession proceedings,
      4:55-57

Gaining possession
   security of tenure and, 1:55
Glass
   description of, 6:32-33
Glass fibre
   use of, 6:53
Grounds for possession. *See*
   Possession

Entries in this volume appear in bold.
1. *Security of Tenure* 2. *Tenants' Rights* 3. *Nuisance and Harassment*
4. *Presenting Possession Proceedings* 5. *Repairs and Maintenance*
6. *Dealing with Disrepair*

Guarantee of tenants. *See*
  Tenants' guarantee

Handwriting expert
  possession proceedings,
    evidence at, 4:73
Harassment
  aims of guide, 3:5-9
  anti-harassment policy,
    3:83-84
  assistance to victim, 3:88-89
  collecting evidence, 3:88
  criminal offences, 3:71-74
  evidence, 3:88
  gang-busting, 3:93
  Housing Corporation, duties
    of, 3:74-75
  injunctions, 3:78-80, 3:91-92
  laws against,
    criminal offences, 3:71-74
    generally, 3:69-70
    Housing Corporation,
      duties of, 3:74-75
    local authorities, duties
      and powers of, 3:74-82
    racial harassment, nature
      and extent of, 3:70-71
  litigation, 3:89-98
  local authorities,
    appearing in proceedings
      brought by others, 3:80
    criminal proceedings, 3:78
    duties of, 3:74-75
    financial assistance,
      provision of, 3:82
    general powers of, 3:76-82
    making bye-laws, 3:81-82
    obtaining injunctions,
      3:78-80
    promoting interests of
      inhabitants, 3:78
    section 222 cases,
      difficulties of, 3:80-81
  meaning, 3:85, 3:100
  monitoring evidence, 3:88
  obtaining possession, 3:93-98

practice in case of, 3:83-98
pre-litigation strategy,
  3:89-98
procedures in case of, 3:83-98
racial, nature and extent of,
  3:70-71
tenancy agreement,
  generally, 3:84-87
  right to buy covenants, 3:87
tort of, 3:33-35
victim, assistance to, 3:88-89
Hazardous materials
  asbestos, 6:52-53
  glass fibre, 6:53
  radon gas, 6:53-54
  urea-formaldehyde foam,
    6:53
Health and safety
  inspection of disrepair,
    6:80-81
  public health. *See* Public
    health
Hearsay evidence
  meaning, 4:156
  possession proceedings,
    4:67-69
Holiday letting
  exclusion, 1:40
  out of season, 1:84
Home
  matrimonial, 1:111-113
  redevelopment, letter relating
    to, 1:133-134
  residence condition, 1:46-51
  tenant unable to take care of,
    1:74-75
  two homes, 1:49-51
  use as, 1:46-51
Homeless persons
  accommodation for, 1:34-35,
    1:42
Hostel accommodation
  assured shorthold lettings,
    1:116
  gaining possession, 1:117-118
  hostel, meaning, 1:117

Entries in this volume appear in bold.
1. *Security of Tenure* 2. *Tenants' Rights* 3. *Nuisance and Harassment*
4. *Presenting Possession Proceedings* 5. *Repairs and Maintenance*
6. *Dealing with Disrepair*

Housing Act 1985, 1:114-115
Housing Act 1988, 1:115-118
shared living
    accommodation, 1:115
tenancy distinguished from
    licence, 1:17-19, 1:114, 1:115
Housing allocation. *See*
Allocation of housing
management. *See*
    Management
stock. *See* Housing stock
Housing action trust
consultation duties, 2:73-74
declaration of,
    consultation, 2:93
    legal status of tenants, 2:94
    possession, grounds for,
        2:94
Housing association
committees, representation
    on, 2:78
contractual succession
    clauses, 2:26-27
local authority development,
    combination with, 2:95
sale tenanted to,
    consultation, 2:92
    legal status of tenants, 2:92
    possession, grounds for,
        2:92-93
sale with vacant possession to,
    consultation, 2:93
    possession, grounds for,
        2:93
secure tenants, functions
    relating to, 2:4
Housing benefit
possession action, defence to,
    4:93-95
rent and, 1:101
Housing manager
witness, as, 5:132-133
Housing stock
building diagrams, 6:147-162
generally, 6:1-2
information on, 2:61

inspection. *See* Inspection of
    disrepair
non-traditional,
    building diagrams,
        6:147-162
    failures in, 6:59-61
    generally, 6:20-21
    high rise, 6:60-61
    large panel systems, 6:21,
        6:59-60
    modern timber-frame, 6:22,
        6:61
    no-fines, 6:22
    prefabricated buildings,
        6:59
    steel and reinforced
        concrete frame, 6:21
traditional. *See* Traditional
    housing stock

Ignorance
private nuisance action,
    defence to, 3:22-23
Illegal occupier
conditions for security of
    tenure, 1:52-53
letter to, 1:131-132
Illegal user
connection between offence
    and premises, 1:73
secure tenant, grounds for
    possession against, 1:73
Immediate order
possession, for, 1:119,
    4:123-124
Implied terms
express terms conflicting
    with, 5:22
Improvements
compensation for, 5:125
rent following, 5:126
repair distinguished from,
    alternative tests, 5:30-31
    generally, 5:25
    test, 5:25-30
social landlord, by, 5:126-127

Entries in this volume appear in bold.
1. *Security of Tenure* 2. *Tenants' Rights* 3. *Nuisance and Harassment*
4. *Presenting Possession Proceedings* 5. *Repairs and Maintenance*
6. *Dealing with Disrepair*

statutory right to improve,
5:124-125
tenant, by,
compensation, 5:125
discretionary payments,
5:125-126
generally, 5:123-124
rent following, 5:126
statutory right to improve,
5:124-125
Inevitable accident
private nuisance action,
defence to, 3:21-22
Informal admission
meaning, 4:156
possession proceedings, 4:69
Information
accommodation applications,
about, 2:58-59
disclosure, exemption from,
2:59
housing allocation, about,
2:57-58
**inspection of disrepair,
preparing for,
background information,
6:71-73
initial information, 6:70-71
recording information,
6:69-71**
landlord authorities,
meaning, 2:56-57
provision of, 2:56
repairing obligations, on,
5:9-10
secure tenants, to,
housing allocations, on,
2:62
housing stock, on, 2:61
management, on, 2:62
obligations relating to,
2:60-63
rents, on, 2:61
repairs, on, 2:61
tenancy files, about, 2:58-59
tenants' guarantee, under,

2:63-65
See also Consultation
Inherited tenancy
possession, grounds for,
1:85-86
Injunction
enforcement through, 5:115
harassment case, in, 3:78-80,
3:91-92
interim, 5:66-67
landlord's remedy for breach,
5:112
meaning, 3:100, 4:156
nuisance case, in,
court, factors taken into
account by, 3:56-59
generally, 3:52-53
interlocutory injunction,
3:54, 3:55-56
mandatory injunction, 3:54
perpetual injunction, 3:54
prohibitory injunction, 3:54
quia timet injunction,
3:54-55
repairs, tenant's remedies
relating to, 5:65-71
types of, 3:54-55
Inquiries and investigations
nuisance, relating to,
collecting evidence, 3:41-43
complaints, 3:39-40
generally, 3:38-39
giving warnings, 3:39-40
noise nuisance, 3:42-43
private investigators, use
of, 3:42
substantiated complaints,
3:39-40
Insect infestation
complaints relating to,
5:60-63
**disease carrying insects,
6:50-51
just unpleasant, 6:51
wood-boring insects, 6:49-50**
Inspection of disrepair

Entries in this volume appear in bold.
1. *Security of Tenure* 2. *Tenants' Rights* 3. *Nuisance and Harassment*
4. *Presenting Possession Proceedings* 5. *Repairs and Maintenance*
6. *Dealing with Disrepair*

appointments, 6:78-80, 6:81-82
background information,
  address, 6:71-72
  building type, 6:72
  common parts, 6:73
  identification code, 6:71-72
  location, 6:72
  occupants, 6:72-73
  preparing for inspection,
    6:71-73
  size of property, 6:72
  tenancy agreement, 6:73
  type of property, 6:72
camera, 6:76
casual call systems, 6:78-80
conduct of,
  generally, 6:82
  introductions, 6:83
  methodical procedure,
    6:84-86
  preliminaries, 6:83-84
diary systems, 6:79-80
do-it-yourself, 6:99-100
equipment,
  basics, 6:74-75
  camera, 6:76
  moisture meter, 6:75-76
health and safety, 6:80-81
information,
  background, 6:71-73
  initial, 6:70-71
  recording, 6:69-71
making appointments,
  6:81-82
methodical procedure,
  generally, 6:84-86
  identifying defects, 6:86
  senses, use of, 6:86
moisture meter, 6:75-76
need for, 6:68-71
notes, 6:87-98
occupied dwellings, 6:68
post-inspection practice,
preparing for,
  background information,
    6:71-73

equipment, 6:74-76
housing manager, role of,
  6:65-67
need for inspection, 6:68-71
occupied dwellings, 6:68
recording information,
  6:69-71
starting points, 6:68
third parties, 6:68
voids, 6:68
purpose of, 6:77-78
reporting,
  core section, 6:106-111
  customers, 6:104
  findings, 6:104-105
  format, 6:106-114
  generally, 6:103
  landlord's liability, 6:113-114
  record note, 6:112-113
  reference to further action,
    6:114
  schedule of defects and
    repairs, 6:107-111
  supplementary sections,
    6:112
  tenant's liability, 6:114
sample table of notes and
  diagnosis, 6:88-93
starting points, 6:68
third parties, 6:68
timescales, 6:98-99
voids, 6:68
whether necessary, 6:68-71
Insulation
  description of, 6:29
Interest
  damages, on, 5:77
Interlocutory
  meaning, 3:100, 4:156
Interlocutory injunction
  nuisance case, 3:54, 3:55-56
Interrogatories
  meaning, 4:156
  possession proceedings,
    4:57-58
Intestacy

Entries in this volume appear in bold.
1. *Security of Tenure* 2. *Tenants' Rights* 3. *Nuisance and Harassment*
4. *Presenting Possession Proceedings* 5. *Repairs and Maintenance*
6. *Dealing with Disrepair*

meaning, 2:100
Investigations. *See* Inquiries
and investigations

Job mobility
accommodation, 1:35-36
Joint tenants
notice to quit, 1:128, 4:33-34
status of, 1:8-9
surrender by, 1:126
termination by, 1:129-130
Judge
possession proceedings, 4:76
reasonableness, discretion
relating to, 1:96-97
Judgments
repairs and maintenance,
relating to, 5:135-136

Land
agricultural, 1:40
development, 1:32-34,
4:35-36
neighbouring, access to,
5:115-116
ownership of,
proof of, 4:22-23
tenancy agreement, proof
of, 4:22-23
trespass to, as private
nuisance, 3:16
Landlord
acts of waste, remedy
against, 5:109
assignment, written consent
to, 2:35-36
change of,
assured tenancy, 1:42
secure tenancy, 1:42
exempt, 1:41
new, acquisition of, 2:74-75
nuisance,
liability for, 3:13-15
responsibility to tackle,
3:12-13
occupier wanted to share or

move, 2:49
pick a landlord, 2:74-75
possession proceedings. *See*
Possession proceedings
reasonableness, interests
relating to, 1:97-98
repairing obligation. *See*
Repairs and maintenance
resident, 1:41
secure tenancy, condition
relating to, 1:30-38
social, repairing obligation
of. *See* Repairs and
maintenance
superior, 1:9
works of, 1:78-79, 1:84-85, 4:41
Landlord authorities
meaning, 2:56-57
Large scale voluntary transfers
(LSVT)
consultation on, 2:71-72
Leading question
meaning, 4:156
Lease
extension of, long
leaseholder's right to
acquire, 1:6-7
long, 1:31-32
Leaseholder. *See* Long
leaseholder
Legal aid
possession proceedings, 4:133
Legal relations
no intention to create, 1:21-24
Letter
annoyance, tenant causing,
to, 1:133
home being redeveloped,
relating to, 1:133-134
illegal occupier, to, 1:131-132
nuisance, tenant causing, to,
1:133
rent arrears, tenant with, to,
1:132
Liability for repair. *See* Repairs
and maintenance

Entries in this volume appear in bold.
1. *Security of Tenure* 2. *Tenants' Rights* 3. *Nuisance and Harassment*
4. *Presenting Possession Proceedings* 5. *Repairs and Maintenance*
6. *Dealing with Disrepair*

Licence
  elderly, accommodation for,
    1:19-20
  hostel accommodation,
    1:17-19, 1:114, 1:115
  residential, 1:10-11
Licensed premises
  security of tenure and, 1:37,
    1:40
Licensee
  meaning, 1:10
  occupiers,
    landlord, position of, 2:49
    wanting to share, 2:48-49
  possession proceedings,
    generally, 4:114-115
    summary possession,
      4:115-119
  residential licence, 1:10-11
  service occupier, 1:24
  status of, 1:10-11
  tenant distinguished from,
    accommodation essential
      for job, 1:24-25
    elderly, accommodation
      for, 1:19-20
    employee, rights of, 1:25-28
    exceptions, 1:20-28
    exclusive possession,
      1:16-17
    generally, 1:14
    hostel accommodation,
      1:17-19, 1:114, 1:115
    legal relations, no intention
      to create, 1:21-24
    service occupier, 1:24
    service tenant, 1:24
    tenancy, elements of,
      1:14-16
    tied accommodation, 1:24
  trespasser distinguished
    from, 1:113
Limitation periods
  breach of contract, 5:78
  negligence, 5:78-79
  tenant's remedies, 5:78-79

Litigation
  harassment, relating to,
    gang-busting, 3:93
    generally, 3:89-91
    injunctions, 3:91-92
    obtaining possession,
      3:93-98
  nuisance, relating to,
    alternatives to, 3:38
    generally, 3:51-52
    injunctions, 3:52-59
    order for possession,
      3:59-68
  possession. *See* Possession
    proceedings
  repair, relating to, costs of,
    5:2-3
Local authority
  Building Act 1984, powers
    under, 5:105
  committees, representations
    on, 2:77
  compulsory competitive
    tendering, 2:89
  contractual succession
    clauses, 2:27-28, 2:29
  drains, powers relating to,
    5:105
  improvements, discretionary
    payment relating to,
      5:125-126
  reasonableness, policy
    relating to, 1:103-104
  redevelopment by,
    consultation, 2:94
    generally, 2:94
    housing association
      development, combined
      with, 2:95
    legal status of tenants,
      2:95
    possession, grounds for,
      2:95
  residents, duty to, 5:93-94
  sanitary facilities, powers
    relating to, 5:104-105

secure tenants, functions
relating to, 2:4-5
sewers, powers relating to,
5:105
statutory nuisance, action
relating to, 3:26-28
suitable alternative
accommodation, certificate
relating to, 1:92, 1:93, 1:94
tenants' management
organisation, support for,
2:83-84
vermin, powers relating to,
5:105
Location
suitable alternative
accommodation, of, 1:95
Lodgers
assured tenant, taken in by,
2:47
conditions for security of
tenure, 1:51-53
deterioration caused by, 1:74
illegal occupation, 1:52-53
loss of security of tenure,
1:51-52
secure tenant, taken in by,
2:40-44
London Housing Survey (1993)
racial harassment, figures on,
3:7
Long leaseholder
assured tenancy, exclusion of,
1:40
extension of lease, right to
acquire, 1:6-7
freehold, right to acquire,
1:6-7
status of, 1:6-7
Loss
secure tenancy, of, 1:122-123

Magistrates' court
statutory nuisance in, 5:135
Maintenance. *See* Repairs and
maintenance

Management
appointment of manager,
5:88-89
balloting,
further ballot, 2:86-87
requirements, 2:85
CCT. *See* Compulsory
competitive tendering
disputes, 2:87-88
feasibility study,
full, 2:85-86
initial, 2:84-85
inspection. *See* Inspection of
disrepair
proposal notice,
balloting, 2:85
right to manage, 2:82-83
withdrawal, 2:88
repairs. *See* Repairs and
maintenance
right to manage,
balloting, 2:85
compulsory competitive
tendering, relationship
with, 2:89
disputes, 2:87-88
full feasibility study,
2:85-86
generally, 2:80-81
initial feasibility study,
2:84-85
local authority support,
2:83-84
notification and further
ballot, 2:86-87
proposal notice, 2:82-83
registration of organisation,
2:89
rights acquired, 2:88
tenants' management
organisations, 2:81-82
withdrawal of notice,
2:88
secure tenants, information
to, 2:62-63
tenants' organisations,

Entries in this volume appear in bold.
1. *Security of Tenure* 2. *Tenants' Rights* 3. *Nuisance and Harassment*
4. *Presenting Possession Proceedings* 5. *Repairs and Maintenance*
6. *Dealing with Disrepair*

disputes, 2:87-88
funding for, 2:78-79
local authority support,
    2:83-84
registration, 2:89
rent levies for tenants'
    funds, 2:79
right to manage, 2:81-82
witness, housing manager as,
    5:132-133
Managing agents
consultation on use of,
    2:69-71
secure tenancy, 1:31
Mandatory injunction
nuisance case, 3:54
Materials of construction
    asphalt, 6:34-35
    bituminous materials, 6:34-35
    brick, 6:26-28
    concrete, 6:30
    enemies of healthy buildings.
        See **Disrepair**
    felt, 6:34-35
    generally, 6:23-24
    glass, 6:32-33
    insulation, 6:29
    metal, 6:33-34
    mortar and pointing, 6:28
    plaster, 6:31
    pointing, 6:28
    render, 6:28-29
    rock, 6:29-30
    slate, 6:31-32
    stone, 6:31
    tiles, 6:32
    timber, 6:24-26
Matrimonial home
cohabitees, 1:111-112
remaining spouse, rights of,
    1:112-113
right to remain in, 1:112
spouses, 1:112-113
Matrimonial property order
secure tenancy, relating to,
    2:11

Mediation
    meaning, 3:100
    nuisance, relating to,
        generally, 3:45-46
        process, 3:46-48
Medical evidence
    possession proceedings,
        4:73-74
Members of family
    succession, 2:13-15
Mesne tenant
    status of, 1:9-10
Metal
    corrosion, 6:51-52
    description of, 6:33-34
Ministers of religion
    possession, grounds for, 1:84
Moisture generation
    users of building, by, 6:54
Money judgment
    order including, 4:126
    proof of, 4:31-32
    unauthorised occupier, action
        against, 4:103-105
Mortar
    description of, 6:28
    pointing, and, 6:28
Mortgaged property
    assured tenant, grounds for
        possession against, 1:84

Negligence
    limitation periods, 5:78-79
    nuisance and, 3:29-31
    repairs, relating to, 5:39,
        5:50-52
Neighbourhood
    nature of, private nuisance
        and, 3:18
Neighbouring land
    access to, 5:115-116
Neighbours
    complaints from, 1:72
New tenancy
    assured shorthold, 1:107
Noise nuisance

Entries in this volume appear in bold.
1. *Security of Tenure* 2. *Tenants' Rights* 3. *Nuisance and Harassment*
4. *Presenting Possession Proceedings* 5. *Repairs and Maintenance*
6. *Dealing with Disrepair*

evidence of, 3:42-43
private nuisance, as, 3:16
Non-housing property
employee, required for, 1:80
Non-traditional housing stock
building diagrams, 6:147-162
failures in, 6:59-61
generally, 6:20-21
high rise, 6:60-61
inspection. *See* Inspection of
disrepair
large panel systems, 6:21,
6:59-60
modern timber-frame, 6:22, 6:61
no-fines, 6:22
prefabricated buildings, 6:59
steel and reinforced concrete
frame, 6:21
Notice
defective premises, relating
to, 5:41-43
forfeiture, of, 1:63-64
repair, relating to,
agent, to, 5:33-35
reasonable time, meaning,
5:35
social landlord's
contractual liabilities,
5:31-35
section 48, 1:68-69
seeking possession,
assured tenancy, 1:61-62,
1:138-142
commencing possession
proceedings, 4:10-13
examples, 1:59-60
generally, 1:58-59
length of, 4:13
meaning, 4:156
secure tenancy, 1:60-61,
1:134-138
Notice to quit
abandoned premises,
1:110-111
form, 1:142-143
generally, 1:108

hostel accommodation,
1:117-118
joint tenants, by, 1:128,
4:33-34
meaning, 4:157
period of notice, 1:109
service, 1:110
tenant, by,
contents, 1:128
effect, 1:129
generally, 1:128
joint tenants, 1:128
Nuisance
agencies used to deal with,
environmental health
officers, 3:49
planning departments,
3:49-50
police, 3:50
RSPCA, 3:50
social services, 3:49
aims of guide, 3:5-9
annoyance and, 3:61-63
assured tenant, grounds for
possession against, 1:88
causes of, 3:2-5
compulsory competitive
tendering of housing
management, 3:43-44
consequences of, 3:2-5
definitions, 3:10-11
evidence, 1:72, 3:41-43
fault, based on, 5:50
inquiries and investigations,
collecting evidence, 3:41-43
complaints, 3:39-40
generally, 3:38-39
giving warnings, 3:39-40
noise nuisance, 3:42-43
private investigator, use of,
3:42
substantiated complaints,
3:39-40
invalid excuses for, 3:23
laws against,
definitions, 3:10-11

Entries in this volume appear in bold.
1. *Security of Tenure* 2. *Tenants' Rights* 3. *Nuisance and Harassment*
4. *Presenting Possession Proceedings* 5. *Repairs and Maintenance*
6. *Dealing with Disrepair*

generally, 3:10
negligence and nuisance,
    3:29-31
private nuisance, 3:15-23
public nuisance, 3:23-24
rule in *Rylands v Fletcher*,
    3:31-33
social landlords'
    responsibility and
    liability, 3:12-15
statutory nuisance, 3:24-29
letter to tenant causing, 1:133
liability for, 3:13-15
litigation,
    alternatives to, 3:38
    generally, 3:51-52
    injunctions, 3:52-59
    order for possession,
        3:59-68
meaning, 3:100, 4:157
mediation,
    generally, 3:45-46
    process, 3:46-48
negligence and, 3:29-31
neighbours, complaints from,
    1:72
noise,
    evidence of, 3:42-43
    private nuisance, as, 3:16
possession proceedings,
    generally, 4:106-109
    proof of nuisance, 4:39
    return date, 4:110
    undertakings, 4:110-112
    witness statement, 4:110
private,
    assessing unreasonable
        use, 3:17-19
    defences, 3:21-23
    generally, 3:15-16
    invalid excuses for, 3:23
    types of, 3:16-17
    who can be sued, 3:20
    who can sue, 3:19-20
probationary tenancies,
    3:44-45

public, 3:23-24
reasonableness in case of,
    1:98-99, 3:64-68
remedies, 5:50
repairs, relating to,
    fault, nuisance based on,
        5:50
    remedies, 5:50
    social landlord's non-
        contractual liabilities,
        5:39, 5:49-50
responsibility to tackle,
    3:12-13
rule in *Rylands v Fletcher*,
    complainant, matters to be
        proved by, 3:31-33
    generally, 3:31
secure tenant, grounds for
    possession against, 1:70-73
social landlord,
    liability of, 3:13-15
    responsibility and liability,
        3:12-15
    responsibility to tackle
        nuisance, 3:12-13
statutory,
    circumstances amounting
        to, 5:91-92
    Environmental Protection
        Act, required action
        under, 3:26-29
    generally, 3:24-25
    magistrates' court, in, 5:135
    nature of nuisance, 5:93
    nuisance, meaning, 3:26
    prejudicial to health,
        3:25-26, 5:92-93
those who live with tenant,
    caused by, 1:71
visitors, caused by, 1:71
who can be sued, 3:20,
    3:36-37
who can sue, 3:19-20, 3:36-37

Oath
    evidence on, 4:77

Entries in this volume appear in bold.
1. *Security of Tenure* 2. *Tenants' Rights* 3. *Nuisance and Harassment*
4. *Presenting Possession Proceedings* 5. *Repairs and Maintenance*
6. *Dealing with Disrepair*

Occupation
  illegal, 1:52-53, 1:131-132
  owner occupier. *See* Owner
    occupier
  sharing,
    landlord wanting occupier
      to share, 2:49
    occupier wanting to share,
      2:48-49
  status of occupier,
    examples, 1:12-13
    generally, 1:5
    licensee, 1:10-11
    owner occupier, 1:5-7
    tenant, 1:7-10
    trespasser, 1:11
  unauthorised occupier,
    meaning, 4:158
Occupied dwelling
  preparing for inspection of,
  6:68
Occupier
  repair, liability for, 5:38,
    5:44-45
Orders
  compensation. *See*
    Compensation
  disrepair, dealing with,
    6:142-143
  possession. *See* Possession
    orders
  repairs and maintenance,
    relating to, 5:135-136
  unless, meaning, 4:158
Outright order
  possession, for, 1:120,
    4:124-125
Overcrowding
  secure tenant, grounds for
    possession against, 1:78
Owner
  land, of,
    proof of, 4:22-23
    tenancy agreement, proof
      of, 4:22-23
  returning home, 1:84

Owner occupier
  long leaseholder,
    extension of lease, right to
      acquire, 1:6-7
    freehold, right to acquire,
      1:6-7
    status of, 1:6-7
  meaning, 1:5-6
  status of, 1:5-7

Participation
  committees, representation on,
    generally, 2:77
    housing authorities, 2:78
    local authorities, 2:77
  rent levies for tenants' funds,
    2:79
  tenants' organisations,
    funding for, 2:78-79
  See also Consultation
Particulars of claim
  meaning, 4:157
  possession proceedings. *See*
    Possession proceedings
Parties
  possession proceedings, 4:20,
    4:138-140
Payments
  compensation. *See*
    Compensation
  tenants, to, 5:120-122
Penetrating damp
  complaints relating to, 5:53-55
Period of notice
  eviction, protection from,
    1:109
Periodic tenancy
  meaning, 2:100, 4:157
  status of tenant, 1:7-8
  statutory, 2:46
  tenancy agreement, 2:54-55
Permanent moves
  getting works done, 5:119
Perpetual injunction
  nuisance case, 3:54
Personal files

Entries in this volume appear in bold.
1. *Security of Tenure* 2. *Tenants' Rights* 3. *Nuisance and Harassment*
4. *Presenting Possession Proceedings* 5. *Repairs and Maintenance*
6. *Dealing with Disrepair*

access to, 2:58-59
Pets
  secure tenant, grounds for
    possession against, 1:70
Plaintiff
  meaning, 4:157
Planning departments
  nuisance, dealing with
    problems of, 3:49-50
Plants
  disrepair caused by, 6:55-56
Plaster
  description of, 6:31
Pleadings
  meaning, 4:157
  possession proceedings,
    4:14-20, 4:55-58
Pointing
  mortar and, 6:28
Police
  nuisance, dealing with
    problems of, 3:50
Possession
  assured shorthold tenancy,
    1:107, 4:113-114
  assured tenant, grounds for
    possession against,
    annoyance, 1:88
    breach of term of tenancy,
      1:87
    deterioration of dwelling-
      house, 1:88
    discretionary grounds,
      1:86-88
    furniture, deterioration of,
      1:88
    generally, 1:83
    holiday letting out of
      season, 1:84
    inherited tenancy, 1:85-86
    landlord's works, 1:84-85
    mandatory grounds, 1:84-86
    ministers of religion, 1:84
    mortgaged property, 1:84
    nuisance, 1:88
    rent arrears, 1:86, 1:87

    returning home owner,
      1:84
    specimen form of order,
      4:150-151
    student letting, 1:84
    suitable alternative
      accommodation, 1:87
    tied accommodation, 1:88
  avoiding formal proceedings,
    1:57-58
  exclusive, 1:16-17
  gaining, 1:55
  harassment case, in, 3:93-98
  hostel accommodation, of,
    1:117-118
  housing action trust,
    declaration of, 2:94
  housing association,
    sale tenanted to, 2:92-93
    sale with vacant
      possession, 2:93
  landlord's remedy for breach,
    5:110-111
  local authority,
    redevelopment by, 2:95
  notice seeking,
    assured tenancy, 1:61-62,
      1:138-142
    commencing possession
      proceedings, 4:10-13
    generally, 1:58-60
    length of, 4:13
    meaning, 4:156
    rent arrears, effect on,
      1:99-100
    secure tenancy, 1:60-61,
      1:134-138
  nuisance case, order in,
    annoyance, nuisance and,
      3:61-63
    generally, 3:59-60
    grounds for possession,
      3:60-64
    procedure, 3:60
    reasonableness in granting
      possession, 3:64-68

Entries in this volume appear in bold.
1. *Security of Tenure* 2. *Tenants' Rights* 3. *Nuisance and Harassment*
4. *Presenting Possession Proceedings* 5. *Repairs and Maintenance*
6. *Dealing with Disrepair*

tenancy agreement, breach
 of, 3:60-61
waste, 3:63-64
orders. *See* Possession orders
proceedings. *See* Possession
 proceedings
reasonableness. *See*
 Reasonableness
rent arrears,
 discretionary grounds, 1:87
 mandatory grounds, 1:86
 proceedings. *See* Possession
  proceedings
requiring tenant to move,
 5:117-118
secure tenant, grounds for
 possession against,
 accommodation pending
  works, 1:77-78
 annoyance, 1:70-73
 breach of other term, 1:70
 charitable purposes, 1:79
 deception, tenancy
  obtained by, 1:75-76
 deterioration of premises,
  1:73-75
 disabled, accommodation
  for, 1:80
 employment related
  accommodation, 1:76-77
 exchange at premium, 1:76
 furniture, deterioration of,
  1:73-75
 grounds1-8, 1:67-78
 grounds9-11, 1:78-79
 grounds 12-16, 1:79-82
 landlord's works, 1:78-79
 non-housing property
  required for employee,
  1:80
 nuisance, 1:70-73
 overcrowding, 1:78
 rent arrears, 1:67-69
 sheltered accommodation,
  1:81
 special needs

 accommodation, 1:80-81
 under-occupation, 1:81-82
seeking,
 avoiding formal
  proceedings, 1:57-58
 fixed term tenancy, 1:62-66
 forfeiture, 1:62-66
 grounds for, 1:56-57
 procedure, 1:58-62
 security provided, 1:56
successor,
 assignee, seeking
  possession against, 2:34-35
 under-occupation by, 2:22
suitable alternative
 accommodation. *See*
 Suitable alternative
 accommodation
under-occupation by
 successor, for, 2:22
warrant for, 1:122, 4:134-135
Possession orders
 acceptance of rent, 1:123
 application to set aside,
  1:123-124
 assured tenancies, 4:150-151
 consent order, 4:126-129
 costs,
  generally, 4:129-130
  interlocutory matters, in,
   4:130-132
  return date, orders at,
   4:132
  types of order, 4:130-132
 enforcement of, 4:126
 generally, 1:119, 4:123
 immediate, 1:119, 4:123-124
 leave, not to be enforced
  without, 4:126
 legal aid, 4:133
 loss of secure tenancy,
  1:122-123
 money judgment, 4:126
 nuisance case, 3:59-68
 outright, 1:120, 4:124-125
 rent arrears cases,

Entries in this volume appear in bold.
1. *Security of Tenure* 2. *Tenants' Rights* 3. *Nuisance and Harassment*
4. *Presenting Possession Proceedings* 5. *Repairs and Maintenance*
6. *Dealing with Disrepair*

arrears at significant level,
4:90-91
arrears cleared, 4:89
arrears substantially
cleared and agreement
about remainder, 4:89-90
options for orders, 4:88-92
very significant arrears,
4:91-92
rented property, 4:152-153
setting aside, 4:137-138
specimen form,
assured tenancy, 4:150-151
possession suspended,
4:152-153
summary possession, 4:119
suspended, 1:101, 1:120-122,
4:125, 4:152-153
warrant for possession, 1:122
Possession proceedings
accelerated procedure, 1:108,
4:114
accommodation,
employees, required for,
4:41-42
pending works, 4:40-41
adjournment,
court's attitude to request,
4:50
defence raised, 4:50-51
generally, 4:48
inability to prove case,
4:48-49
return date, change of
circumstances before,
4:49-50
affidavit,
evidence, 4:71-72
meaning, 4:154
summary possession, 4:116
aim of book, 4:1-3
annoyance, based on,
generally, 4:106-109
proof of, 4:39
return date, 4:110
undertakings, 4:110-112

witness statement, 4:110
appeal, 4:136-137
assured shorthold tenants,
accelerated possession
procedure, 4:114
generally, 4:113-114
burden of proof, 4:65-66, 4:154
calculation of court time, 4:64
checklists,
death of tenant, 4:33
generally, 4:32
loss of security of tenure,
4:32-33
notice to quit by joint
tenant, 4:33-34
security of tenure,
exceptions to, 4:34-37
statutory grounds for
possession, claims based
on, 4:37-43
choice of court, 4:13-14
closing speeches, 4:81
commencing,
choice of court, 4:13-14
generally, 4:7
parties, 4:20
pleadings, 4:14-20
steps before action, 4:7-8
summons, 4:14-20
termination of tenancy
agreement, 4:8-13
consent order, 4:126-129
consolidation, 4:51-52,
4:51-52
costs,
generally, 4:129-130
interlocutory matters, in,
4:130-132
return date, orders at, 4:132
types of order, 4:130-132
County Court Rules, 4:3
cross-examination, 4:79-80,
4:155
death of tenant, 4:33
defence,
case, 4:80-81

Entries in this volume appear in bold.
1. *Security of Tenure* 2. *Tenants' Rights* 3. *Nuisance and Harassment*
4. *Presenting Possession Proceedings* 5. *Repairs and Maintenance*
6. *Dealing with Disrepair*

disrepair as, 4:92-93
housing benefit as,
    4:93-95
Landlord and Tenant Act
    1987, under, 4:95
rent arrears cases, 4:92-95
return date, raised at,
    4:45-46, 4:50-51
unauthorised occupier,
    action against, 4:98-103
deterioration of premises,
    4:39-40
development land, 4:35-36
directions,
    calculation of court time,
        4:64
    generally, 4:54-55
    meaning, 4:155
    typical, 4:63-64
discovery,
    exceptions, 4:60
    filing, 4:58-59
    lists, by, 4:59
    meaning, 4:155
    pretrial procedure, 4:58-60
disrepair as defence, 4:92-93
employees, accommodation
    required for, 4:41-42
environmental health officer,
    evidence of, 4:72-73
evidence,
    affidavit, 4:71-72, 4:154
    burden of proof, 4:65-66,
        4:154
    Civil Evidence Act, under,
        4:70-71
    evidence-in-chief, 4:78-79,
        4:155
    expert, 4:72-74
    generally, 4:65
    giving, 4:77
    hearsay, 4:67-69, 4:156
    informal admission, 4:69,
        4:156
    medical, 4:73-74
    oath, on, 4:77

public documents, 4:69-70
    rent arrears cases, 4:87-88
    types of, 4:66-74
    unauthorised occupier,
        action against, 4:97-98
expert evidence,
    environmental health
        officers, 4:72-73
    generally, 4:72
    handwriting experts, 4:73
    medical evidence, 4:73-74
    surveyors, 4:73
forms, 4:143-153
further action,
    appeal, 4:136-137
    generally, 4:134
    setting aside order,
        4:137-138
    stay of execution, 4:137
    subsequent conduct by
        parties, 4:138-140
    warrant for possession,
        4:134-135
further and better particulars,
    meaning, 4:155-156
    pretrial procedure, 4:55-57
handwriting expert, evidence
    of, 4:73
hearsay evidence, 4:67-69,
    4:156
housing benefit as defence,
    4:93-95
informal admission, 4:69,
    4:156
interrogatories,
    meaning, 4:156
    pretrial procedure, 4:57-58
judges, 4:76
Landlord and Tenant Act
    1987, defence under, 4:95
landlord's case,
    cross-examination, 4:79-80
    evidence-in-chief, 4:78-79
    re-examination, 4:80
legal aid, 4:133
licensees,

generally, 4:114-115
summary possession,
4:115-119
limited security,
assured shorthold,
4:113-114
licensees, 4:114-119
medical evidence, 4:73-74
money judgment,
order including, 4:126
proof of, 4:31-32
unauthorised occupier,
action against, 4:103-105
notice to quit,
joint tenant, by, 4:33-34
meaning, 4:157
nuisance, based on,
generally, 4:106-109
proof of, 4:39
return date, 4:110
undertakings, 4:110-112
witness statement, 4:110
oath, evidence on, 4:77
opening, 4:77
orders. *See* Possession orders
ownership of land,
proof of, 4:22-23
tenancy agreement, proof
of, 4:22-23
particulars of claim,
content of, 4:17-20
meaning, 4:157
rent arrears cases, 4:18-20,
4:144-147
specimen form, 4:144-147
parties,
commencing proceedings,
4:20
subsequent conduct by,
4:138-140
pleadings,
commencing proceedings,
4:14-20
meaning, 4:157
pretrial procedure, 4:55-58
pretrial procedure,

directions, 4:54-55, 4:63-64
generally, 4:53-54
procedural steps, 4:55-62
unless orders, 4:62-63
proof,
burden of, 4:65-66, 4:154
checklists, 4:32-43
inability to prove case,
4:48-49
money judgments, 4:31-32
ownership of land, 4:22-23
reason for seeking
possession, 4:26-31
return date, 4:47-52
tenant's interest,
termination of, 4:23-25
unauthorised occupier,
action against, 4:98
what needs to be proved,
4:21-43
re-examination, 4:80, 4:157
reason for seeking possession,
landlord's circumstances,
4:27-28
non-secure/assured
tenants, 4:26
reasonableness, 4:26-28
secure/assured tenants,
4:26
suitable alternative
accommodation, 4:28-31
tenant's circumstances, 4:27
rent arrears cases,
arrears at significant level,
4:90-91
arrears cleared, 4:89
arrears substantially
cleared and agreement
about remainder, 4:89-90
defences, 4:92-95
disrepair as defence,
4:92-93
evidence of arrears, 4:88
generally, 4:85
housing benefit as defence,
4:93-94

Entries in this volume appear in bold.
1. *Security of Tenure* 2. *Tenants' Rights* 3. *Nuisance and Harassment*
4. *Presenting Possession Proceedings* 5. *Repairs and Maintenance*
6. *Dealing with Disrepair*

Landlord and Tenant Act
 1987, defence under, 4:95
orders, options for, 4:88-92
particulars of claim,
 4:18-20, 4:144-147
required evidence, 4:87-88
statutory grounds for
 possession, 4:37-39,
  4:85-87
very significant arrears,
 4:91-92
return date,
 adjournments, 4:48-51
 annoyance, action based
  on, 4:110
 change of circumstances
  before, 4:49-50
 consolidation, 4:51-52
 costs orders at, 4:132
 defences raised at, 4:45-46,
  4:50-51
 generally, 4:44
 inability to prove case,
  4:48-49
 meaning, 4:157
 nature of hearing, 4:44-47
 nuisance, action based on,
  4:110
 proving case, 4:47-52
 typical outcomes at, 4:46-47
 unauthorised occupier,
  action against, 4:105-106
security of tenure,
 exceptions to, 4:34-37
 loss of, 4:32-33
service,
 summary possession,
  4:117-118
 tenant's interest,
  termination of, 4:23-25
setting aside order, 4:137-138
settlement, 4:76
short-life user property,
 4:35-36
specimen forms, 4:143-153
statutory grounds for

possession, claims based on,
accommodation pending
 works, 4:40-41
annoyance to neighbours,
 4:39
deterioration of premises,
 4:39-40
employees,
 accommodation required
 for, 4:41-42
landlord's works, 4:41
nuisance to neighbours,
 4:39
rent arrears, 4:37-39
under-occupation, 4:42-43
stay of execution, 4:137
subleasing schemes, 4:36-37
suitable alternative
 accommodation,
 landlords who are not local
  authorities, 4:30-31
 local authority tenants,
  4:29-30
 proof of, 4:28-31
summary possession,
 affidavit, 4:116
 hearing, 4:118-119
 named respondent, service
  on, 4:117
 order, 4:119
 procedure, 4:115
 unknown persons, service
  on, 4:117-118
summons,
 commencing proceedings,
  4:14-20
 content of, 4:17
 meaning, 4:158
 specimen form, 4:143
surveyor, evidence of, 4:73
tenant's interest, termination of,
 deceased tenants, 4:25
 form of notice, 4:23
 physically serving notice,
  4:24-25
 proof of, 4:23-25

service of notice, 4:23-25
termination of tenancy
agreement,
generally, 4:8-9
length of notice, 4:13
notice seeking possession,
4:10-13
tied accommodation, 4:34-35
trial,
closing speeches, 4:81
cross-examination, 4:79-80
defence case, 4:80-81
evidence-in-chief, 4:78-79
giving evidence, 4:77
judges, 4:76
landlord's case, 4:78-80
oath, evidence on, 4:77
opening, 4:77
outline, 4:75-76
re-examination, 4:80
settlement, 4:76
typical directions, 4:63-64
unauthorised occupier,
defences, 4:98-100
generally, 4:96-97
meaning, 4:96, 4:158
money judgment, 4:103-105
new tenancy, creation of,
4:100-103
proof in court, 4:98
required evidence, 4:97-98
return date, 4:105-106
spouses, rights of, 4:98
temporarily absent tenant,
4:98-100
under-occupation, 4:42-43
undertaking,
annoyance, action based
on, 4:110-112
meaning, 4:158
nuisance, action based on,
4:110-112
specimen form, 4:148-149
unless order,
meaning, 4:158
pretrial procedure, 4:62-63

warrant for possession,
4:134-135
witness statements,
annoyance, action based
on, 4:110
meaning, 4:158
nuisance, action based on,
4:110
pretrial procedure, 4:60-62
works,
accommodation pending,
4:40-41
landlord, of, 4:41
Post-inspection practice. *See*
Inspection of disrepair
Premises
meaning, 5:43-44
Premium
exchange at, 1:76
Preparing for inspection. *See*
Inspection of disrepair
Pretrial procedure. *See*
Possession proceedings
Principal home
secure tenancy, 2:12-13
Private investigator
nuisance, investigation of,
3:42
Private nuisance
assessing unreasonable use,
behaviour of perpetrator,
3:18
damage, 3:18
generally, 3:17-18
neighbourhood, nature of,
3:18
generally, 3:15-16
invalid excuses for, 3:23
types of, 3:16-17
who can be sued, 3:20
who can sue, 3:19-20
Probationary tenancy
nuisance, solution to problem
of, 3:44-45
Prohibitory injunction
nuisance case, 3:54

Entries in this volume appear in bold.
1. *Security of Tenure* 2. *Tenants' Rights* 3. *Nuisance and Harassment*
4. *Presenting Possession Proceedings* 5. *Repairs and Maintenance*
6. *Dealing with Disrepair*

Proof
  assignment, of, 2:33-34
  burden of, meaning, 4:154
  possession proceedings. *See*
    Possession proceedings
Property transfer order
  assignment pursuant to, 2:32
Protection from eviction. *See*
  Eviction, protection from
Public health
  Building Act 1984, 5:105
  drains, 5:105
  duties relating to, 5:90-105
  environmental protection. *See*
    Environmental protection
  sanitary facilities, 5:104-105
  sewers, 5:105
  vermin, 5:105
Public nuisance
  common law, at, 3:23-24
  criminal offence, as, 3:23

Quia timet injunction
  nuisance case, 3:54-55
Quiet enjoyment
  breach of covenant for, 5:38,
    5:46-47
  meaning, 3:100-101, 4:157

Racial harassment
  extent of, 3:70-71
  London Housing Survey
    (1993) figures on, 3:7
  nature of, 3:70-71
  See also Harassment
Rateable values
  high, tenancy of premises
    with, 1:39
Re-examination
  meaning, 4:157
  possession proceedings, 4:80
Reason for seeking possession.
  See Possession proceedings
Reasonableness
  breach of other term,
    1:102-103

circumstances to be
  considered, 1:97-99
council policy, 1:103-104
generally, 1:96
granting possession, 3:64-68
judge's discretion, 1:96-97
landlord, interests of, 1:97-98
nuisance cases, 1:98-99,
  3:64-68
possession, reason for
  seeking, 4:26-28
private nuisance,
  assessing unreasonable
    use, 3:17-19
  behaviour of perpetrator,
    3:18
  damage, 3:18
  neighbourhood, nature of,
    3:18
reasonable time, meaning,
  5:35
remedying breach, 1:102-103
rent arrears,
  amount, 1:99
  disrepair, counterclaims
    for, 1:100-101
  example, 1:101-102
  generally, 1:99
  housing benefit, rent and,
    1:101
  notice seeking possession,
    effect of, 1:99-100
  reasons for arrears, 1:100
  suspended orders, 1:101
repair, legal requirements
  relating to, 5:5-6
tenant, interests of, 1:97
Receiver
  appointment of, 5:88-89
Records
  inspection of disrepair,
    preparing for, 6:69-71
Redecoration
  damages for, 5:76-77
  disrepair, dealing with,
    6:132-133

Entries in this volume appear in bold.
1. *Security of Tenure* 2. *Tenants' Rights* 3. *Nuisance and Harassment*
4. *Presenting Possession Proceedings* 5. *Repairs and Maintenance*
6. *Dealing with Disrepair*

repairing obligation and, 5:31
Redevelopment. *See* Estate
  redevelopment
Refuse
  disposal of, 6:55
Registration
  tenants' management
    organisation, of, 2:89
Remedies
  breach of other term,
    1:102-103
  nuisance, for, 5:50
  repairs, relating to,
    damages, 5:71-77
    direct action, 5:81-85
    duty to mitigate, 5:79-81
    injunctions, 5:65-71
    limitation periods, 5:78-79
    manager, appointment of,
      5:88-89
    nuisance, 5:50
    receiver, appointment of,
      5:88-89
    right to repair, 5:85-88
    secure tenants, rights of,
      5:85-88
    specific performance,
      5:65-71
    tenant, of, 5:64-89
Render
  description of, 6:28-29
Rent arrears
  earlier, 1:68
  forfeiture action based on,
    1:65
  letter to tenant with, 1:132
  possession,
    discretionary grounds, 1:87
    mandatory grounds, 1:86
    proceedings. *See* Possession
      proceedings
  reasonableness relating to,
    amount, 1:99
    counterclaims for disrepair,
      1:100-101
    example, 1:101-102
    generally, 1:99

housing benefit, rent and,
  1:101
notice seeking possession,
  effect of, 1:99-100
reasons for arrears, 1:100
suspended orders, 1:101
reasons for, 1:100
section 48 notice, 1:68-69
secure tenant, grounds for
  possession against, 1:67-69
Rents
  arrears. *See* Rent arrears
  improvement, following,
    5:126
  repairs, use to pay for, 5:84-85
  secure tenants, information
    to, 2:61
  set-off against, 5:81
  tenants' funds, rent levies for,
    2:79
Repairs and maintenance
  access to neighbouring land,
    5:115-116
  acts of waste, 5:108-109
  agent,
    liability of, 5:10-11
    notice to, 5:33-35
  asbestos, 5:59-60
  breach , landlord's remedies
    for,
    damages, 5:111-112
    generally, 5:109-110
    injunctions, 5:112
    possession of premises,
      5:110-111
  breach of contract, 5:78
  breach of covenant for quiet
    enjoyment, 5:38, 5:46-47
  cockroaches, 5:60-63
  common parts liability,
    5:22-24
  complaints,
    asbestos, 5:59-60
    cockroaches, 5:60-63
    common types of, 5:53-63
    damp, 5:53-57
    insect infestation, 5:60-63

Entries in this volume appear in bold.
1. *Security of Tenure* 2. *Tenants' Rights* 3. *Nuisance and Harassment*
4. *Presenting Possession Proceedings* 5. *Repairs and Maintenance*
6. *Dealing with Disrepair*

roofs, 5:58-59
subsidence, 5:57-58
condensation dampness,
   5:56-57
contractual liabilities of social
   landlord,
      agent, liability of, 5:10-11
      common parts liability,
         5:22-24
      existence of contract, 5:9
      express contractual
         obligations, 5:16-18
      exterior, 5:12-14
      generally, 5:7-9
      implied contractual
         obligations, 5:19-22
      information, 5:9-10
      Landlord and Tenant Act
         1985 s11, 5:11-16
      nature of repair, 5:24-31
      notice, 5:31-35
      repair, meaning, 5:24-31
      standard of repair, 5:14-16
      structure and exterior,
         5:12-14
      summary, 5:35-36
      who is liable, 5:10-11
contractual obligations of
   tenant,
      generally, 5:106-107
      tenant-like user, 5:107
      waste, acts of, 5:108-109
costs of litigation, 5:2-3,
   5:102-103
counterclaims, set-off and,
   5:82-83
court proceedings,
      choice of court, 5:128-129
      court etiquette, 5:131
      evidence, 5:129-131,
         5:132-134
      experts' evidence,
         5:133-133
      generally, 5:128
      housing manager as
         witness, 5:132-133
      judgments, 5:135-136

orders, 5:135-136
procedure, 5:131-132
statutory nuisance in
   magistrates' court, 5:135
witness, housing manager
   as, 5:132-133
damages,
      general, 5:73-76
      interest, 5:77
      landlord's remedy for
         breach, 5:111-112
      redecoration, for, 5:76-77
      special, 5:72-73
      tenant's remedy, as, 5:71-77
damp,
      complaints relating to,
         5:53-57
      condensation, 5:56-57
      penetrating, 5:53-55
      rising, 5:55-56
defective premises,
      Act of 1972, 5:39-44, 5:47-48
      notice, 5:41-43
      premises, meaning, 5:43-44
      relevant defect, meaning,
         5:40-41
      summary of provisions,
         5:38
direct action,
      set-off against rent, 5:81
      set-off and counterclaims,
         5:82-83
      using rent to pay for
         repairs, 5:84-85
disrepair. *See* Disrepair
duty to mitigate, 5:79-81
enforcement through
   injunction, 5:115
entry to repair,
      access to neighbouring
         land, 5:115-116
      enforcement through
         injunction, 5:115
      rights relating to, 5:114-116
environmental protection. *See*
   Environmental protection
   evidence,

Entries in this volume appear in bold.
1. *Security of Tenure* 2. *Tenants' Rights* 3. *Nuisance and Harassment*
4. *Presenting Possession Proceedings* 5. *Repairs and Maintenance*
6. *Dealing with Disrepair*

court proceedings, in,
5;129-131
experts, of, 5:133-134
housing manager, of,
5:132-133
existence of contract, 5:9
experts' evidence, 5:133-134
express contractual
obligations,
implied obligations,
conflict with, 5:22
interpretation of express
terms, 5:16-18
social landlord, of, 5:16-18
exterior, 5:12-14
failure to carry out works,
5:70-71
financial incentives,
costs of litigation, 5:2-3
generally, 5:2
getting works done, 5:113-122
housing manager as witness,
5:132-133
implied contractual
obligations,
express terms, conflict
with, 5:22
repair v. renewal, 5:19-22
social landlord, of, 5:19-22
improvement distinguished
from repair,
alternative tests, 5:30-31
generally, 5:25
test, 5:25-30
improvements,
generally, 5:123
social landlord, by,
5:126-127
tenant, by, 5:123-126
information on, 5:9-10
injunctions,
enforcement through, 5:115
failure to carry out works,
5:70-71
generally, 5:65-66
interim, 5:66-67
landlord's remedy for

breach, 5:112
insect infestation, 5:60-63
inspecting disrepair. *See*
Disrepair
judgments, 5:135-136
Landlord and Tenant Act 1985,
applicability of s11,
5:11-12
applicability of s8, 5:45-46
exclusions, 5:12
pre-October 24, 1961, 5:12
standard of repair, 5:14-16
structure and exterior,
5:12-14
legal requirements,
generally, 5:4
reasonableness, 5:5-6
social landlords, 5:4-5
limitation periods,
breach of contract, 5:78
negligence, 5:78-79
tenant's remedy, as, 5:78-79
litigation, costs of, 5:2-3,
5:102-103
magistrates' court, statutory
nuisance in, 5:135
manager, appointment of,
5:88-89
materials of construction. *See*
Materials of construction
nature of repair,
alternative tests, 5:30-31
generally, 5:24-25
improvement
distinguished from
repair, 5:25
redecoration, 5:31
test, 5:25-30
negligence,
limitation periods,
5:78-79
social landlord's non-
contractual liabilities,
5:39, 5:50-52
neighbouring land, access to,
5:115-116
non-contractual liabilities of

Entries in this volume appear in bold.
1. *Security of Tenure* 2. *Tenants' Rights* 3. *Nuisance and Harassment*
4. *Presenting Possession Proceedings* 5. *Repairs and Maintenance*
6. *Dealing with Disrepair*

social landlord,
Defective Premises Act
1972, 5:39-44, 5:47-48
generally, 5:37-39
Landlord and Tenant Act
1985 s8, 5:45-46
negligence, 5:39, 5:50-52
nuisance, 5:39, 5:49-50
Occupiers' Liability Act
1957, 5:44-45
quiet enjoyment, breach of
covenant for, 5:46-47
notice,
agent, to, 5:33-35
defective premises, relating
to, 5:41-43
disrepair, of, 5:31-35
reasonable time, 5:35
nuisance,
fault, based on, 5:50
magistrates' court,
statutory nuisance in,
5:135
non-contractual liabilities,
5:39, 5:49-50
remedies, 5:50
occupier, liability of, 5:38,
5:44-45
orders, 5:135-136
payments to tenants,
5:120-122
penetrating damp, 5:53-55
permanent moves, 5:119
**planned maintenance,
6:122-124**
possession of premises,
grounds for, 5:110-111,
5:117-118
landlord's remedy for
breach, 5:110-111
requiring tenant to move,
5:117-118
prescribed periods, meaning,
5:87-88
public health. *See* Public health
qualifying repairs, meaning,
5:86

quiet enjoyment, breach of
covenant for, 5:38, 5:46-47
reasons for repair,
financial incentives, 5:2-3
generally, 5:1
legal requirements, 5:4-6
physical condition of
property, importance of,
5:1
receiver, appointment of,
5:88-89
redecoration,
damages for, 5:76-77
**disrepair, dealing with,
6:132-133**
obligation to repair and,
5:31
remedies,
breach, for, 5:109-112
damages, 5:71-77,
5:111-112
direct action, 5:81-85
duty to mitigate, 5:79-81
injunctions, 5:65-71, 5:112
landlord, of, 5:109-112
limitation periods, 5:78-79
manager, appointment of,
5:88-89
nuisance, for, 5:50
possession of premises,
5:110-111
receiver, appointment of,
5:88-89
right to repair, 5:85-88
secure tenants, rights of,
5:85-88
specific performance,
5:65-71
tenant, of, 5:64-89
waste, acts of, 5:109
renewal v. repair, 5:19-22
rent,
set-off against, 5:81
use to pay for repairs,
5:84-85
reporting repairs, 5:86-87
requiring tenant to move,

Entries in this volume appear in bold.
1. *Security of Tenure* 2. *Tenants' Rights* 3. *Nuisance and Harassment*
4. *Presenting Possession Proceedings* 5. *Repairs and Maintenance*
6. *Dealing with Disrepair*

generally, 5:116-117
permanent moves, 5:119
possession, grounds for,
    5:117-118
security of tenure, 5:118
temporary moves,
    5:119-120
right to repair,
    prescribed periods,
        meaning, 5:87-88
    qualifying repairs,
        meaning, 5:86
    reporting repairs, 5:86-87
    secure tenants, 5:85-88
rising damp, 5:55-56
roofs, 5:58-59
secure tenants,
    information to, 2:61
    right to repair, 5:85-88
security of tenure, 5:118
set-off,
    counterclaims, and, 5:82-83
    rent, against, 5:81
short-term, 6:136
specific performance,
    agreeing works, 5:69-70
    evidence, 5:69-70
    generally, 5:65-66
    limits to, 5:67-68
    resisting application,
        5:68-69
specification for repairs,
    6:116-117
standard of repair, 5:14-16
stock of housing. *See*
    Housing stock
structure and exterior, 5:12-14
subsidence, 5:58-59
temporary moves, 5:119-120
tenant's remedies,
    damages, 5:71-77
    direct action, 5:81-85
    generally, 5:64-65
    injunctions, 5:65-71
    limitation periods, 5:78-79
    manager, appointment of,
        5:88-89

receiver, appointment of,
    5:88-89
right to repair, 5:85-88
secure tenants, rights of,
    5:85-88
specific performance,
    5:65-71
tenant-like user, 5:107
value for money, 6:127-128
waste, acts of, 5:108-109
wholesale redevelopment or
    rehabilitation, 6:124-127
witness, housing manager as,
    5:132-133
works,
    agreeing, 5:69-70
    entry to repair, 5:114-116
    failure to carry out, 5:70-71
    getting works done,
        5:113-122
    variations of, 6:133-134
See also Disrepair
Reporting
    disrepair, dealing with,
        core section, 6:106-111
        customers, 6:104
        findings, 6:104-105
        format, 6:106-114
        generally, 6:103
        landlord's liability, 6:113-114
        record note, 6:112-113
        reference to further action,
            6:114
        schedule of defects and
            repairs, 6:107-111
        supplementary sections,
            6:112
        tenant's liability, 6:114
    repairs, 5:86-87
Residence condition
    security of tenure, 1:43,
        1:46-51
    succession, 2:15-19
Resident landlord
    assured tenancy, exemption
        from, 1:41
Residential licence

Entries in this volume appear in bold.
1. *Security of Tenure* 2. *Tenants' Rights* 3. *Nuisance and Harassment*
4. *Presenting Possession Proceedings* 5. *Repairs and Maintenance*
6. *Dealing with Disrepair*

meaning, 1:10-11
Residents
  local authority duty to,
    5:93-94
Return date
  meaning, 4:157
  possession proceedings. *See*
    Possession proceedings
Returning home owner
  possession, mandatory
    grounds for, 1:84
Right to buy covenants
  harassment, prevention of,
    3:87
Right to manage. *See*
  Management
Rights of tenants
  ancillary, summary of, 2:3-4
  assignment. *See* Assignment
  assured tenant,
    generally, 2:5-6
    tenants' guarantees, 2:6-7
  consultation. *See*
    Consultation
  historical background,
    ancillary rights, summary
      of, 2:3-4
    assured tenant, 2:5-7
    generally, 2:1
    secure tenant, subsequent
      changes for, 2:4-5
    Tenants' Charter 1980, 2:2-4
  information. *See* Information
  management. *See*
    Management
  participation. *See*
    Participation
  succession. *See* Succession
Rising damp
  complaints relating to,
    5:55-56
Rock
  description of, 6:29-30
Roofs
  chimneys, 6:14-15
  complaints relating to,
    5:58-59

diagrams, 6:155-158
fire walls, 6:14-15
gables, 6:14
hips, 6:14
parapets, 6:14-15
pitched,
  chimneys, 6:14-15
  fire walls, 6:14-15
  front to rear, 6:14
  gables, 6:14
  hips, 6:14
  nature of, 6:13
  parapets, 6:14-15
  slates, 6:15-16
  tiles, 6:15-16
  valley roofs, 6:13-14
  valleys, 6:14
  slates, 6:15-16
  tiles, 6:15-16
  valley, 6:13-14
  valleys, 6:14
Rot
  dry, 6:47-48
  wet, 6:48-49
Royal Society for Prevention of
  Cruelty to Animals (RSPCA)
  nuisance, dealing with
    problems of, 3:50
Rylands v Fletcher, rule in
  nuisance and, 3:31-33

Sanitary facilities
  local authority, powers of,
    5:104-105
Section 48 notice
  secure tenant, grounds for
    possession against, 1:68-69
Secure tenancy
  assignment of,
    exchange, by way of,
      2:35-39
    generally, 2:32
    mutual exchange, 2:35-39
    potential successor, to,
      2:32-33
    proof of assignment,
      2:33-34

Entries in this volume appear in bold.
1. *Security of Tenure* 2. *Tenants' Rights* 3. *Nuisance and Harassment*
4. *Presenting Possession Proceedings* 5. *Repairs and Maintenance*
6. *Dealing with Disrepair*

property transfer order,
2:32
successor assignee, seeking
possession against,
2:34-35
change of landlord, 1:42
conditions, 1:43-44
consultation with secure tenants,
acquisition by new
landlord, 2:74-75
basic requirement, 2:65
generally, 2:65
housing action trusts,
2:73-74
large scale voluntary
transfers, 2:71-72
managing agents, use of,
2:69-71
matters requiring
consultation, 2:66-69
method of consultation,
2:65-66
other duties, 2:69-75
outcome of consultation,
2:69
redevelopment scheme,
declaration of, 2:72-73
exceptions,
accommodation pending
works, 1:37
agricultural holdings, 1:37
almshouses, 1:38
business lettings, 1:38
development land, 1:32-34
employee accommodation,
1:32
generally, 1:31
homeless persons,
accommodation for,
1:34-35
job mobility
accommodation, 1:35-36
licensed premises, 1:37
long lease, 1:31-32
student lettings, 1:37-38
subleasing scheme,
1:36-37

forfeiture of, 1:65
generally, 1:29
housing association,
functions of, 2:4
information to secure tenants,
housing allocations, on,
2:62
housing stock, on, 2:61
management, on, 2:62
obligations, 2:60-63
rents, on, 2:61
repairs, 2:61
landlord,
change of, 1:42
condition, 1:30-38
local authority, functions of,
2:4-5
lodgers, 2:40-44
loss of, 1:122-123
managing agents, 1:31
meaning, 2:100, 3:101, 4:158
notice seeking possession of,
1:60-61, 1:134-138
possession, grounds for,
accommodation pending
works, 1:77-78
annoyance, 1:70-73
breach of other term, 1:70
charitable purposes, 1:79
deception, tenancy
obtained by, 1:75-76
deterioration of premises,
1:73-75
disabled, accommodation
for, 1:80
employment related
accommodation, 1:76-77
exchange at premium, 1:76
furniture, deterioration of,
1:73-75
grounds 1-8, 1:67-68
grounds 9-11, 1:78-79
grounds 12-16, 1:79-82
landlord's works, 1:78-79
non-housing property
required for employee,
1:80

Entries in this volume appear in bold.
1. *Security of Tenure* 2. *Tenants' Rights* 3. *Nuisance and Harassment*
4. *Presenting Possession Proceedings* 5. *Repairs and Maintenance*
6. *Dealing with Disrepair*

nuisance, 1:70-73
overcrowding, 1:78
pets, 1:70
rent arrears, 1:67-69
sheltered accommodation, 1:81
special needs
    accommodation, 1:80-81
under-occupation, 1:81-82
waiver of breach, 1:70
repair, right to,
    generally, 5:85
    prescribed periods,
        meaning, 5:87-88
    qualifying repairs,
        meaning, 5:86
    reporting repairs, 5:86-87
spouse of tenant, 2:13
subletting, 2:39-40
succession,
    common law, succession at,
        2:10
    deceased tenant already
        successor, 2:19-21
    fixed term tenancy, 2:22
    generally, 2:10
    Housing Act 1985, under,
        2:11-21, 2:97
    matrimonial property
        order, 2:11
    only or principal home,
        2:12-13
    other members of family,
        2:13-15
    residence condition, 2:15-19
    spouse of tenant, 2:13
    succession to whom, 2:21
    termination, 2:10-11
    under-occupation by
        successor, possession for,
        2:22
    who may succeed, 2:11-12
suitable alternative
    accommodation,
    allocation policy, 1:91-92
    generally, 1:89-90
    local authority certificate,
        1:92

needs of tenant, 1:90-91
tenancy agreement, 2:50-54
to whom, 2:21
under-occupation by
    successor, possession for,
    2:22
who may succeed, 2:11-12,
    2:25
Security of tenure
    conditions. *See* Conditions for
        security of tenure
    getting works done, 5:118
    lodgers, 2:47-48
    main purpose of book, 1:2-3
    meaning, 1:1
    possession proceedings. *See*
        Possession proceedings
    subtenants, 2:47-48
    summary of legislation,
        1:1-2
Seeking possession
    avoiding formal proceedings,
        1:57-58
    fixed term tenancy, 1:62-66
    forfeiture, 1:62-66
    grounds for, 1:56-57
    procedure, 1:58-62
    security provided, 1:56
Separation
    property transfer order, 2:32
Service
    notice to quit, of, 1:110
Service occupier
    meaning, 1:24
Service tenant
    meaning, 1:24
Set-off
    counterclaims, and, 5:82-83
    rent, against, 5:81
Setting aside
    possession order, 4:137-138
Settlement
    possession proceedings, 4:76
Sewers
    local authority, powers of,
        5:105
Shared accommodation

Entries in this volume appear in bold.
1. *Security of Tenure* 2. *Tenants' Rights* 3. *Nuisance and Harassment*
4. *Presenting Possession Proceedings* 5. *Repairs and Maintenance*
6. *Dealing with Disrepair*

security of tenure, conditions for, 1:45-46

Sheltered accommodation
secure tenant, grounds for possession against, 1:81

Slate
description of, 6:31-32
roofs, 6:15-16

Smells
private nuisance, as, 3:16

Snow
disrepair caused by, 6:57

Social landlord
improvements by, 5:126-127
repairing obligation of. *See* Repairs and maintenance

Social services
nuisance, dealing with problems of, 3:49

Special needs accommodation
secure tenant, grounds for possession against, 1:80-81

Specific performance
evidence, 5:69-70
limits to, 5:67-68
repairs, tenant's remedies relating to, 5:65-71
resisting application, 5:68-69

Spouses
matrimonial home, rights relating to, 1:112-113
succession, requirements for, 2:13
suspended order, powers relating to, 1:121

Squatters
nature of, 1:113
status of, 1:11

State of affairs
private nuisance, as, 3:17

Status of occupier
examples, 1:12-13
generally, 1:5
housing action trust, declaration of, 2:94
housing association, sale tenanted to, 2:92

licensee,
generally, 1:10
residential licence, 1:10-11

local authority,
redevelopment by, 2:95

owner occupier,
long leaseholder, 1:6-7
owner, meaning, 1:5-6

tenant,
assignment of tenancy, 1:8
fixed term, 1:7-8
generally, 1:7
joint tenants, 1:8-9
periodic tenancy, 1:7-8
subtenants, 1:9-10
succession to tenancy, 1:8
transfer of tenancy, 1:8
written agreement, 1:8

trespasser, 1:11

Statutory authorisation
private nuisance action, defence to, 3:22

Statutory grounds for possession. *See* Possession proceedings

Statutory nuisance
circumstances amounting to, 5:91-92
Environmental Protection Act, required action under, individual 'person aggrieved', action by, 3:28-29
local authority, action by, 3:26-28
generally, 3:24-25
magistrates' court, in, 5:135
nature of nuisance, 5:93
nuisance, meaning, 3:26
prejudicial to health, 3:25-26, 5:92-93

Statutory periodic tenancy
assignment, 2:46

Stay of execution
possession proceedings, 4:137

Steps before action
possession proceedings, 4:7-8

Entries in this volume appear in bold.
1. *Security of Tenure* 2. *Tenants' Rights* 3. *Nuisance and Harassment*
4. *Presenting Possession Proceedings* 5. *Repairs and Maintenance*
6. *Dealing with Disrepair*

Stock of housing. *See* Housing stock

Stone
   description of, 6:31

Structure
   meaning, 5:13
   repairing obligation, 5:12-14

Student lettings
   assured tenancy, exclusion from, 1:40
   possession, grounds for, 1:84
   secure tenancy, exclusion from, 1:37-38

Subleasing scheme
   possession proceedings, 4:36-37
   secure tenancy, 1:36-37

Subletting
   assured tenancy, 2:46
   conditions for security of tenure, 1:51-53
   illegal occupation, 1:52-53
   loss of security of tenure, 1:51-52
   secure tenancy, 2:39-40

Subsidence
   complaints relating to, 5:57-58

Subtenants
   deterioration caused by, 1:74
   lodgers distinguished from, 2:41-44
   security of, 2:47-48
   status of, 1:9-10

Succession
   assured tenancy,
     common law, succession at, 2:23-24
     contractual succession clauses, 2:26-30
     generally, 2:23
     Housing Act 1988, succession under, 2:24-25
     who is successor, 2:25
     who succeeds, 2:25
   common law, at, 2:10, 2:23-24

   contractual clauses,
     alternative approach, 2:29-30
     enforceability of right of assignment, 2:28-29
     generally, 2:26
     housing association, 2:26-27
     local authority, 2:27-28, 2:29
   deceased tenant already successor, 2:19-21
   effects of, 2:9-10
   generally, 2:8-9
   meaning, 1:8
   members of family, 2:13-15
   only or principal home, 2:12-13
   potential successor, assignment to, 2:32-33
   residence condition, 2:15-19
   secure tenancy,
     common law, succession at, 2:10
     deceased tenant already successor, 2:19-21
     fixed term tenancy, 2:22
     generally, 2:10
     Housing Act 1985, succession under, 2:11-21, 2:97
     matrimonial property order, 2:11
     only or principal home, 2:12-13
     other members of family, 2:13-15
     residence condition, 2:15-19
     spouse of tenant, 2:13
     succession to whom, 2:21
     termination, 2:10-11
     under-occupation by successor, possession for, 2:22
     who may succeed, 2:11-12
   spouse of tenant, 2:13
   successor assignee, seeking possession against, 2:34-35

Entries in this volume appear in bold.
1. *Security of Tenure* 2. *Tenants' Rights* 3. *Nuisance and Harassment*
4. *Presenting Possession Proceedings* 5. *Repairs and Maintenance*
6. *Dealing with Disrepair*

to whom, 2:21
under-occupation by
successor, possession for,
2:22
who may succeed, 2:11-12,
2:25
Suitable alternative
accommodation
assured tenant,
comparison with local
authority practice, 1:94
furniture, 1:94
generally, 1:93
local authority certificate,
1:93
location, 1:95
reluctant tenants, 1:94-95
suitability, 1:93-94
generally, 1:89
possession,
discretionary grounds for,
1:87
proceedings, 4:28-31
secure tenant,
allocation policy, 1:91-92
generally, 1:89-90
local authority certificate,
1:92
needs of, 1:90-91
Sulphates
disrepair caused by, 6:46
Summary possession. *See*
Possession proceedings
Summons
commencing possession
proceedings, 4:14-20
meaning, 4:158
possession proceedings,
commencing proceedings,
4:14-20
content, 4:17
specimen form, 4:143
Sun
disrepair caused by, 6:58
Surrender
agreement to surrender,
1:125

conditions for security of
tenure, 1:53-54
examples, 1:126-128
joint tenants, by, 1:126
nature of, 1:125
operation of law, by, 1:126
Surveyor
possession proceedings,
evidence at, 4:73
Suspended order
court, powers of, 1:120-121
discharge, 1:122
nature of, 1:120
possession, for, 1:101,
1:120-122, 4:125, 4:152-153
rent arrears case, 1:101
spouses, 1:121
terms, 1:121
varying terms, 1:121

Temperature and climate
drought, 6:56-57
frost, 6:57
snow, 6:57
sun, 6:58
Temporary moves
getting works done,
5:119-120
Tenancy
agreement,
assured tenancy, 2:54-55
breach of, as ground for
possession, 3:60-61
changing terms of, 2:50-55
covenant, meaning, 2:99
fixed term tenancy, 2:54
harassment, prevention of,
3:84-87
inspection of disrepair,
preparing for, 6:73
periodic tenancy, 2:54-55
secure tenancy, 2:50-54
termination of, 4:8-13
assignment of. *See*
Assignment
assured. *See* Assured tenancy
change of landlord, 1:42

Entries in this volume appear in bold.
1. *Security of Tenure* 2. *Tenants' Rights* 3. *Nuisance and Harassment*
4. *Presenting Possession Proceedings* 5. *Repairs and Maintenance*
6. *Dealing with Disrepair*

Crown, 1:41

deception, obtained by,
1:75-76

elements of, 1:14-16

exceptions, 1:20-28

files, information about,
2:58-59

fixed term. *See* Fixed term
tenancy

inherited, 1:85-86

landlord,
change of, 1:42
condition, 1:30-38

legal relations, no intention
to create, 1:21-24

periodic. *See* Periodic tenancy

probationary, 3:44-45

rights of tenants. *See* Rights
of tenants

secure. *See* Secure tenancy

Street v Mountford, 1:15-16

succession to. *See* Succession

surrender of, 1:53-54

transfer of, 1:8

**Tenant satisfaction survey
disrepair, dealing with,
6:131-132**

nuisance, causes of, 3:4

Tenants
assignment of tenancy, 1:8
environmental protection,
action relating to,
generally, 5:94
person aggrieved, 5:94-95
person responsible, 5:95-99
fixed term tenancy, 1:7-8
guarantee. *See* Tenants'
guarantee
improvements by,
compensation, 5:125
discretionary payments,
5:125-126
generally, 5:123-124
rent following, 5:126
statutory right to improve,
5:124-125
joint. *See* Joint tenants

licensee distinguished from,
accommodation essential
for job, 1:24-25

elderly, accommodation
for, 1:19-20

employee, rights of, 1:25-28

exceptions, 1:20-28

exclusive possession,
1:16-17

generally, 1:14

hostel accommodation,
1:17-19, 1:114, 1:115

legal relations, no intention
to create, 1:21-24

service occupier, 1:24

service tenant, 1:24

tenancy, elements of,
1:14-16

tied accommodation, 1:24

mesne, 1:9-10

payments to, 5:120-122

periodic tenancy, 1:7-8

possession proceedings. *See*
Possession proceedings

reasonableness, interests
relating to, 1:97

repairing obligation. *See*
Repairs and maintenance

rights. *See* Rights of tenants

service, 1:24

status of, 1:7-10

subtenants, 1:9-10

succession to tenancy, 1:8

termination by,
generally, 1:125
joint tenants, 1:126.
1:129-130
notice to quit, 1:128-129
surrender, 1:125-128

transfer of tenancy, 1:8

unable to take care of home,
1:74-75

written agreement, 1:8

**Tenants' guarantee
disrepair, dealing with,
6:120**

enforcement powers, 2:6-7

Entries in this volume appear in bold.
1. *Security of Tenure* 2. *Tenants' Rights* 3. *Nuisance and Harassment*
4. *Presenting Possession Proceedings* 5. *Repairs and Maintenance*
6. *Dealing with Disrepair*

information under, 2:63-65
regulated areas, 2:6
Tenants' management
organisations
disputes, 2:87-88
funding for, 2:78-79
local authority support for, 2:83-84
registration, 2:89
right to manage, 2:81-82
See also Management
Termination by tenant
joint tenants,
generally, 1:129-130
surrender by, 1:126
notice to quit,
contents, 1:128
effect, 1:129
generally, 1:128
joint tenants, 1:128
surrender,
agreement to surrender, 1:125
examples, 1:126-128
generally, 1:125
joint tenants, by, 1:126
operation of law, by, 1:126
Termination of tenancy
agreement
commencing possession
proceedings, 4:8-13
length of notice, 4:13
notice seeking possession, 4:10-13
Third parties
inspection of disrepair,
preparing for, 6:68
Tied accommodation
possession proceedings, 4:34-35
security of tenure and, 1:24, 1:88
Tiles
description of, 6:32
roofs, 6:15-16
Timber

description of, 6:24-26
ground floors, 6:17
modern timber-frame
construction, 6:22, 6:61
wood-boring insects, 6:49-50
Timescales
inspection of disrepair, 6:98-99
Tort
harassment, of, 3:33-35
meaning, 3:101
nuisance, of, 3:10
Traditional housing stock
building diagrams, 6:147-162
damp-proofing,
basements, 6:19
generally, 6:18
ground floors, 6:19
walls, 6:18
external walls,
blockwork, 6:11
cavity brickwork, 6:10
solid brickwork, 6:10
floors,
above ground level, 6:16-17
boards, 6:18
damp-proofing, 6:19
diagrams, 6:159-160
sheets, 6:18
solid ground floors, 6:17
timber ground floors, 6:17
foundations,
brick footings, 6:12
diagrams, 6:152-154
piling, 6:13
raft, 6:13
reinforced concrete, 6:13
strip, 6:12
timber plates, 6:12
generally, 6:8-9
inspection. See Inspection of
disrepair
internal walls, 6:11
roofs,
diagrams, 6:155-158
flat, 6:16

Entries in this volume appear in bold.
1. *Security of Tenure* 2. *Tenants' Rights* 3. *Nuisance and Harassment*
4. *Presenting Possession Proceedings* 5. *Repairs and Maintenance*
6. *Dealing with Disrepair*

pitched, **6:13-16**
stud partitions, 6:11
walls,
    blockwork, 6:11
    cavity brickwork, 6:10
    damp-proofing, 6:18
    diagrams, 6:148-151
    external, 6:10-11
    internal, 6:11
    solid brickwork, 6:10
    stud partitions, 6:11
windows,
    casements, 6:19-20
    diagrams, 6:160-161
    replacements, 6:20
    sliding sashes, 5:19
Transfer of tenancy
  security of tenure and, 1:8
Trees
  disrepair caused by, 6:55-56
Trespass to land
  private nuisance, as, 3:16
Trespasser
  county court procedure,
    1:113
  licensee distinguished from,
    1:113
  meaning, 1:11
  nature of, 1:113
  status of, 1:11
  unauthorised occupier,
    meaning, 4:158
  See also Unauthorised
    occupier
Trial
  possession proceedings. *See*
    Possession proceedings
Two homes
  security of tenure, conditions
    for, 1:49-51

Unauthorised occupier
  meaning, 4:158
  possession proceedings. *See*
    Possession proceedings
  See also Trespasser
Under-occupation

possession proceedings,
  4:42-43
secure tenant, grounds for
  possession against, 1:81-82
Underground threats
  disrepair caused by, 6:58
Undertaking
  annoyance, possession action
    based on, 4:110-112
  meaning, 4:158
  nuisance, possession action
    based on, 4:110-112
  specimen form, 4:148-149
Unless order
  meaning, 4:158
  possession proceedings,
    4:62-63

Variation
  suspended possession order,
    terms of, 1:121
Vermin
  cockroaches,
    complaints relating to,
      5:60-63
    private nuisance, as, 3:17
  insect infestation, 5:60-63,
    6:49-51
  local authority, powers of,
    5:105
Victim
  harassment, of, assistance to,
    3:88-89
Voids
  preparing for inspection of,
    6:68

Waiver of breach
  forfeiture and, 1:64
  secure tenant, grounds for
    possession against, 1:70
Walls
  blockwork, 6:11
  cavity brickwork, 6:10
  cavity construction for,
    6:44-45
  damp-proofing, 6:18

Entries in this volume appear in bold.
1. *Security of Tenure* 2. *Tenants' Rights* 3. *Nuisance and Harassment*
4. *Presenting Possession Proceedings* 5. *Repairs and Maintenance*
6. *Dealing with Disrepair*

diagrams, **6:148-151**
external,
  blockwork, 6:11
  cavity brickwork, 6:10
  solid brickwork, 6:10
internal, 6:11
solid brickwork, 6:10
stud partitions, 6:11
Warnings
  nuisance, relating to, 3:39-40
Warrant
  possession, for, 1:122,
  4:134-135
Waste
  acts of, tenant's contractual
  obligations relating to,
  5:108-109
  possession, ground for,
  3:63-64
Water
  above ground, 6:43
  construction, from, 6:46
  dampness from ground,
    bridging, 6:41
    lateral penetration, 6:39-40
    remedial damp-proofing,
      6:40-41
    residual, 6:42-43
    rising damp, 6:38-39
    salts, 6:42-43
  disrepair caused by, 6:37-46
  from above,
    cavity construction for
      walls, 6:44-45
    generally, 6:44
  from inside,
    condensation, 6:45
    interstitial condensation,
      6:46
  moisture generation, 6:54
Windows
  casements, 6:19-20
  diagrams, 6:160-161
  replacements, 6:20
  sliding sashes, 6:19
Wiring
  faulty, as private nuisance, 3:17

Witness
  housing manager as,
  5:132-133
  statements. *See* Witness
  statements
Witness statements
  meaning, 4:158
  possession proceedings,
    annoyance, action based
    on, 4:110
    nuisance, action based on,
    4:110
    pretrial procedure, 4:60-62
Wood. *See* Timber
Works
  accommodation pending,
  1:37, 1:77-78, 4:40-41
  agreeing, 5:69-70
  failure to carry out, 5:70-71
  landlord, of, 1:78-79, 1:84-85,
  4:41
  variations of, 6:133-134
Written agreement
  tenancy, relating to, 1:8

Entries in this volume appear in bold.
1. *Security of Tenure* 2. *Tenants' Rights* 3. *Nuisance and Harassment*
4. *Presenting Possession Proceedings* 5. *Repairs and Maintenance*
6. *Dealing with Disrepair*